Some Lovely Islands

other books by Leslie Thomas

autobiography
THIS TIME NEXT WEEK

novels
THE VIRGIN SOLDIERS
ORANGE WEDNESDAY

in preparation
THE LOVE BEACH

Frontispiece
Fair Isle at harvest time
by Stewart Wilson

Some Lovely Islands

by Leslie Thomas

COWARD-McCANN, Inc., NEW YORK

To Lois
with love

SOME LOVELY ISLANDS

First American Edition 1969

Copyright © *Leslie Thomas* 1968

Library of Congress Catalog Card No. 69–18321

Printed in Great Britain

Contents

Fair I.

Auskerry

Luing

Holy I.

at Blasket

llig Michael

Clear I.

Caldy I.

Lundy I.

St. Agnes
& the Gugh

Herm

Introduction LUNDY

A Beginning and an End

It was Lundy that began it. Lundy, the tubby island; the
blue whale of the Bristol Channel.

As a schoolboy I had seen it out on the distant water, fat,
wonderful, mysterious. I had seen it both from the head of
Devon and the foot of Wales. Always it looked blue and I
wondered at what point on the voyage out there the blue
turned to green. Or perhaps, I thought, it did not change;
that when you arrived it really *was* an island of deep blue.
What a thing that would have been! In those days they used
to say, on both the top and bottom sides of the Channel, that
if you could see Lundy it was going to rain, and if you
couldn't see it then it was already raining.

It was years before I went to my childhood island. Before
I made that little voyage I was to stand on islands in the
China Sea, in the Indies, in the Caribbean, and many other
places. They were hot and tropical with idle beaches and
palms. But before I went to Lundy I had never been on a
real island.

It's true that different people see places differently. I was discussing Lundy with a Trinity House captain at Swansea who goes out to provision the lighthouses there and to change over the men at the lights. There are easier places to reach in winter and this was winter. I asked him what he thought of my dream island. He sniffed into the wind running in with the tide. "Well, boy," he said, very Welsh, "it's not exactly the ruddy Madeira of the Bristol Channel, is it?"

The day I first went there it was with summer at its highest. For a week, every morning, I had been going with my children down to the beach at Croyde in North Devon and there she was out there in the ocean sunshine, blue and big as ever. I gazed at her as I had done when I was a boy. Then, on the second Monday I could stand it no longer. I abandoned the family, jumped into my car and drove like mad to Ilfracombe where I was the last one that morning to buy a ticket for the day-trip to Lundy Island. After I'd got my change the lady pulled down the shutter of the little wooden box office with the finality of a guillotine. With my ticket in my hand I went up the gangplank of the pleasure steamer and they pulled it in right after me. You can't leave it any later than that.

I remembered these pleasure boats. Campbells. Before the war they used to run paddle steamers from Newport, down the cocoa Usk to distant and exotic places like Weston-super-Mare, which sounded like Hollywood (and still does). But my mother had discouraged me from anything connected with the sea because the family for generations had all been sailors and, in her opinion, not one of them had come to any good. So I never went.

But here I was, on this brilliant morning in my thirty-second year, voyaging to Lundy with three hundred trippers who broiled under the Bristol Channel sun, licked ice cream and drank pop. Children ran about the deck and mothers screamed. Men put handkerchiefs over their heads. The ship's loudspeaker was playing maritime music and right opposite me two young lovers were going near the bounds of decency, even mid-summer decency, on a life-raft capable (it said) of saving fourteen souls.

I cared nothing, I heard nothing, I saw nothing. Nothing, that is but that blue hump on the top of the sea getting closer, and if anything bluer. I watched it with as much intensity as if I had been alone on the pleasure boat, or for that matter clinging to a lump of cork and on my last cast-away gasp. Say it did stay blue! That would be a laugh, not to mention a shock. But no, it couldn't be or the word would have got around.

Nevertheless my careful recollection of that morning was that it didn't turn colour until we were less than a mile away, and then it became rock-grey topped with green.

We went alongside it like one small ship edging close to a big one. At the southern anchorage there was a lighthouse looking strangely like a policeman. Later that day I asked one of the lighthouse men how you clean the windows of a lighthouse and he said you clean them like any other windows, with a chamois leather and a bucket of water. I didn't believe him and I still don't, but at all the lighthouses I've visited since I've never had the nerve to ask the question again in case I get the same answer.

They send out little boats to take you ashore on Lundy because there is no landing stage. They drop you on the beach and when they dropped me I simply stood there for a moment and looked quietly. Kids were charging about and ramming spades into the innocent sand, dads were shouting about picnic baskets and mums were trying to get out of the tender boats without showing their knickers. But I merely stood. For this was an island, a *true* island, not one of those sticky palm-tree places. And at last I was on it.

It was a marvellous day, hot all the time, with birds flying

about and such a limitless sky for them too. At the top of the
first cliff path I looked down at my boat, far more elegant
from above, placed royally on a sea of August blue, with the
small tenders making seams in the water as they went back
and forth with more passengers.

Somehow I lost everyone else. All three hundred of them,
or whatever the number was. Some of them, I heard later,
never moved from the beach because older or wearier mums
and dads couldn't manage the cliff path. Certainly not many
went beyond the village and the post office. All they really
did was to buy puffin stamps and look at the graves of the
Lundy giant and his wife. You couldn't blame them because
it was very hot.

But I went on, across the bounding grass, over the
quarter wall, the half-way wall, and the three-quarter wall,
to the old middle lighthouse and the newer one at the
northern nose of the island. I had the whole place to myself.
I could see South Wales and imagine myself back there,
looking over here all those years ago. Well, it wasn't
blue. That was settled anyway. Any Welsh or Devonian
child who thinks Lundy is blue should make a note of
this.

I saw seals for the first time in my life, far below on the
sea-washed rocks, and I had the screams of the sea-birds in
my ears for a long time; in fact they are still there now. Then
I poked about among the coves and caves of the pirates and
smugglers who used this as a terminus in the far days. I had
a bottle of beer and some sandwiches sitting on a giddy cliff-
top. I got so sunburned that my face peeled for days.

When I went back to the south anchorage the children
were crying because they had to leave their sandcastles.
Dads were clouting their ears, mothers were collecting bits
into baskets and then trying to clamber into the little boats
without showing their knickers. The lighthouse men waved,
no doubt with relief, and we sailed grandly for Ilfracombe

again with me standing at the stern watching the island return to blue in the evening.

* * *

That settled it. I had seen and sampled briefly something remote and different, a life of land surrounded by sea. I had watched secret seals, heard the birds call, felt the strange joy of loneliness and been brushed by a free wind.

One year, I promised, I will go to other small islands, perhaps ten, around the coasts of these British Isles. Inhabited, deserted, wild, cosy, in any and all weathers. I would find them, discover how to get to them — and go. All through the metropolitan winters I read books written about islands, I drew maps with great care, so that I knew the landing places, the lighthouses, the hamlets and the tracks. Landbound, rushing through life as a newspaperman, my thoughts were very often in those small places of the sea.

In the late spring of 1967 I embarked on this journey I had dreamed about. I went to the Railway Lost Property Office in The Haymarket and bought an anorak with a hood. It was the best thing I have ever bought. Then I got myself a good camera and set off west for my first discoveries.

It was April, and the islands were St. Agnes and The Gugh in the Scillies. In June I was on Caldy, off Pembrokeshire, July high up in the northern seas at Fair Isle and Auskerry. In August I took the whole family to Tralee and from there I journeyed alone to the three lovely Irish isles, Great Blasket, Skellig, and Clear Isle. I was on Herm, in the Channel Isles in October, Luing in the Hebrides in November, and, at the conclusion, Holy Isle, off Northumberland, with the snow of December lying on the beaches.

What a journey. Thinking back on it now, the islands themselves and the people of the islands, I know I have memories to give me pleasure for all my days. In all those truly outlandish places I met nothing but kindness, peace and good humour. I am an expert at very little. I am not a naturalist, a botanist, nor a geologist, and the things I do not know about the sea would fill an ocean. I learned only by asking questions and if the birdwatchers of Fair Isle, the sailors of the Scillies, or the wise men of Clear Isle, sometimes thought they were talking to some half-wit then they never showed it. All I had to go on this unique voyage of discovery was some sense of human nature and a sincere love of remote and secret places.

I call it a unique journey but it is only now, as I write this, that I have become aware that it probably is so. Men have visited all these isles, of course, but I do not believe that anyone has been to ten such widely flung islands in the space of a single year. At a guess, Fair Isle must be seven hundred miles from Herm; St. Agnes and Luing, on about the same line of longitude are five hundred miles as geese fly, while Holy Isle and Cape Clear are extremes east and west.

At the start of the journey I had the fear that one island would be much like the rest. It was only a half-fear, no, even less than that, and it was completely unfounded as I hope these essays show. I would emphasise that these *are* essays, impressions only. On some islands I stayed a week, on others only a single, short day. So anyone looking for a guidebook or a deep social or biological study had better look further along the shelves. Instead I offer you an attempt to capture the beauty, adventure, and humour that I found and enjoyed.

My friend David Eliades took time off from Fleet Street to accompany me to Fair Isle and Auskerry. He was supposed to take some pictures.

One of the epics he took on Fair Isle, a study involving a cow and a church, would, I am certain, win first prize in an exhibition of boring photographs. So he was not a lot of use, except that he was very courageous making the journey at all because he is a rotten sailor and he was being sick into a cold sea when he could have been on holiday at Nice or Lyme Regis, or somewhere. But he made everyone laugh a lot on Fair Isle, not the least by his somewhat unmentionable additions to British bird names, which he made up himself. My thanks to him.

The man who was sea-sick going to Herm (who would think we're an island race!) was Tony Griffiths, who nevertheless recovered to take a lot of photographs and actually get one in the book. He fell down a few holes on Herm and was chased by a mad sheep, but he was very brave and cheerful about it all.

Stewart Wilson, who keeps the island shop on Fair Isle, took the tremendous colour picture which is the jacket of this book, and also the beautiful contrast of harvest and lighthouse which is the frontispiece. He is a quiet and modest man but I think these are thrilling photographs of which he can be very proud.

My thanks too to the Irish Tourist Board, the National Trust for Scotland and the Scottish Tourist Board, to Trinity House, and, most particularly to the British Travel Association and an old friend David Jones of that excellent organisation. Thanks also to Danny and Wendy Hick on The Gugh in the Scillies, to Father Stephen at the monastery on Caldy, to Roy Dennis and his wife on Fair Isle, to John and Pat Dennison at Stronsay in the Orkneys, to the O'Donoghue family on Clear Isle, to John Stringer at Herm, Donald MacDougal and John Brown and the others who live on Luing, and to Clinker, Bash, Old Robert and the rest of the people at Lindisfarne. I thank them for their hospitality, their help and their humour.

I wrote this book as I went along on the journey. From its beginnings in April it has taken me three-quarters of a year. As I write these last lines it is a few minutes before midnight on Christmas Eve, 1967.

A Donkey on the Beach

That evening, on that little island, the sea pushed against the sand bar. It was one of those times when you could imagine the wind just about raising itself up on one elbow to blow a puff or two across the land.

The donkey called Cuckoo was quiet for once, after a day of chasing terrified dogs across the sand and pebbles. National Assistance, the cat, puffed round with love for the donkey, had butchered a rabbit and had brought half of it for Cuckoo to eat if he wanted. He didn't.

From the house on The Gugh I looked across the narrow arm of sand, sweet and white, that tied, at lowest tide, the islet to the island. The people over on St. Agnes were in their houses now and had shut their doors for the night. Granny Spin and old Captain Dick Legge, Miss Quick, the birdwatcher, and the others were inside with lights burning, confidently expecting the late wind to come and make the windows shiver. It was not yet dark, only going on towards it. The last of the daylight came over, skimming the sea and wrapping itself around the old, retired, lighthouse which St. Agnes wears like a white hat, pointed and a bit pointless.

The donkey left the half-rabbit and the cat who sat in stunned disappointment. Cuckoo jolted down to have a look at the sea, and to hear its evening flopping, first on one side of the bar and then on the other. Danny Hick came from the house and we stood for a while watching the donkey. "The day I got married last August," said Danny, "I spent the whole morning with my best man and my two brothers chasing that bloody donkey around the island. Wendy and I went to the church over on Agnes in a gig with Cuckoo pulling. We had to time the service so that the tide wasn't in. Thank God Cuckoo didn't see any dogs on the way. Over on St. Mary's the boatmen had notices up saying 'Wedding on St. Agnes. All beer free,' and plenty of people came."

*   *   *

Strange how loneliness is the one thing I fear in life and yet it is the lonely places that call me, draw me, summon me to go to them and to see and share their loneliness.

Defenceless, stupidly aching with the experience of it, I sat that April for hours on the rim of St. Agnes, the outrider of the Scillies, in the sun and the buoyant wind, looking out across the many western rocks. The grass above the short cliffs was coarse, there were gulls and guillemots among the crevices and over the moving sea.

Far out, towards the Bishop Rock, were the last fragments of England, awash in a cold ocean. Around me, below my feet in the coves and channels, and above my shoulders, rising among the brilliant gorse, the rocks and boulders hung and clung. Some were like puddings, some like ships; a chancel below was being fashioned by the tides, and up there a stony Queen Victoria sniffed at the sea air.

Long before I came to these islands I loved them, read

about them, looked at pictures, and composed, as a boy, an ode about them. My poem, I remember, harboured the epic lines:

> Out there with seal and poutin' puffin,
> The people live right next to nuffin.

An island, a small island like this and with few people, is the one place where you can shout and laugh to yourself and nobody thinks you are mad. Do it in a desert and they think the sun has got you; on top of a mountain and they think you want to be rescued.

Nor would there be much satisfaction in those situations, but on the lip of an island, with only a few boulders and the Bishop Rock lighthouse between you and Gander, Newfoundland, you can call and guffaw or do a dance and nobody gives a damn. You don't feel mad because, unlike in a desert or on a mountain, you have the seabirds and the ocean and the wind for company. The gulls may pause in their patterns to take note of you, but they don't think it odd, because they do the same, noisy things themselves.

Down on the furthest edge of St. Agnes there is strong evidence of man's eccentricity in such a full but lonely place. Two hundred years ago a lighthouse-keeper constructed a delicate maze of pebbles set into the sturdy cliff-top grass. He made a strong job of it for it is complete today and you can totter around it until you are dizzy and in danger of tipping yourself into the ocean. Nobody knows why the keeper built the maze, or what happened to him. Perhaps he used to trot around the tight circles celebrating a solitary summer solstice, encouraged by the gulls to go faster and faster, his arms flapping, his toes jumping, until one second he was there, and the next he was gone, with only the staring birds to witness what had befallen him. Or maybe he grew old in the lighthouse service and retired to Penzance or Saltburn-by-the-Sea. I don't know.

Although it was April it was like summer away from the cliff wind. Grouped about its retired lighthouse, which the Trinity House men, God bless them, were repainting even though it has been no use for donkey's years, are cottages set into thick lanes, a shop, and a school with four pupils.

"The saddest thing here," Wendy Hick, Danny's wife, had told me, "is that once the children reach eleven they go away from the island, and it's for ever. Everyone knows that. They go to boarding school on the mainland and after that they find jobs and make their life over there. They never return."

The hedgerows of that comfortable island were stuffed with flowers and there were bees in the nettles of the church-yard. For me there is always a poignant moment, sharp as a dart, when I hear children's voices coming from the open doorway of a school. Today they were reciting, all four of them, and their small words wandered out into the afternoon lane with its pockets of sunshine, its early summer smells and its warm bumbling noises.

In the end the path — the islanders call it 'the road' because they built it — led nowhere. It buried its nose under the salty sand beside the church. Some men were shaving a keel just there and lobster pots, round skeletons, were littered about.

"Been 'aving scientific experiments with catching lobsters over on the mainland," said one of the men. "They reckon to catch a lot of lobsters too." He sniffed and stared at the old pots as if doubting if he would live to see any change on St. Agnes.

Over his shoulder was the church which the people built years ago from driftwood and island rock. Somehow they forgot to consecrate it, and when the fault was discovered the Bishops had to grant a special licence, reaching back into the years, so that men and their wives could lie legally and so that the dead would not be too restless.

Under their squares of grass, daisies and nettles buried perhaps in their seaboots, are all the Hicks and the Legges of long ago. A little wall cossets them from the wind that homes to the white sand bay from the western rocks. Obediah, James, Stephen, their wives Sue and Annie, their children and theirs too, born, lived and died in this small place.

They knew stirring days. In the islands the St. Agnes folk were called Turks because they were stubby and wide with coal-black eyes and hair. Their speech, it was said, was short and crisp and they grew long silken beards. Their gigs were out among the choppy islets supplying passing ships, helping themselves from wrecks, and in notorious years, provoking the event themselves.

Good and bad they all lie about the churchyard with their feet resting and their hairy ears no longer tuned to the sad and subtle changes of the sea.

They had a life-boat on the island once and its exploits are listed beside the altar in the gaunt church — just above the giant box of Bryant & May's which snuggles to the side of the Cross, ready to light the Sunday candles. In November 1896, it relates, the boat went to the aid of the schooner *Ocean Belle* of Beaumaris, and in September 1903 to the barque *Queen Mab* of Glasgow, while one Christmas Day the crew, dinners on their chins and waistcoats, no doubt, rowed to rescue *Iron Barge No.* 100.

What people they were, those who lived then in that minor universe of isles. Robert Maybee, a salty Shakespeare, bursting with the great love of living:

"When I was young I many times wished I had been a scholar, that I might have written a long history of the Scilly Islands; but being no scholar and in fact, unable to read or write, it was useless my thinking of making a book, so I gave up all idea of it until the year 1883 . . . at that time, and in the evenings, when I had leisure, walking around the hills and thinking of what had passed on the islands in my life-time, I found that I could remember everything that had happened in the islands for sixty-eight years just as if it had occurred on that day.

"It then came into my mind that I would have a little book written if I could get someone to write it for me as I told it to him, about changes in life and trade and ship-wrecks and loss of life and also some pieces of poetry of my own composition. . . .

"I asked the master of the house at which I lodged whether he would write a little book for me in the winter evenings and he was agreeable. The first line of this book was put to paper on 5th November 1883, my age at that time being seventy-four years. . . ."

The people are still like that. Careful and poetic. Old Captain Dick Legge had his hand shaken by the Queen Mother once and she politely asked the venerable Trinity House man if he was a flower farmer.

Crunching a bilious pipe between his historic gums he gurgled, chuckled, and eventually came out with: "O-ah, O-ee. O-ah, O-ee. I loike grows a few liddle daisies, ma'am."

Then Granny Spin. I walked the hedged lane below the schoolhouse and the lighthouse, and there she was, facing the sun in her cottage garden. Her chair had tired of rocking and the flowered garden seemed to close around her, protecting her frail shoulders, the blooms deep and thick and pungent as spice. They call her Granny Spin because she once turned a patient spinning wheel and the children used to watch from the garden gate.

But she doesn't see well now and has to dodge the children as they run in the lane. It's just as well there are only four of them these days or she would have a hard time. She's deaf too and she can only feel the sun and smell the heaped flowers. She sleeps beautifully as the radio, right next to her ear, bawls blatant pop songs. The sound staggers among the green branches and the many flowers like a city drunk in a country orchard, scaring the working bees, no doubt, and drifts eventually down the lane to the beach, the upturned boats, and Cuckoo chasing yet another dog.

Danny calls like the youth he is, his strong voice travelling over the strand. He's driving his tractor to meet the daily launch. Wendy is clutching behind, jolted on a short trailing truck like a Roman on a chariot. They've got to get to the launch for their household supplies and their letters, then back again across to The Gugh before the tide arrives. They had a boat once. But one night they thought a storm was going to bring the house down about their bed. They clutched each other beneath the blankets and went out fearfully in the windy dawn and saw that their boat had been carried away as a prize by the gale. Now they have to watch the tides carefully and if the bar is covered — but not too deeply and dangerously — Danny has to carry Wendy on his back through the water's rush. Then he has to go back for the groceries.

Wendy was engaged to another man once, but he came down and took a sniff at the islands and said he didn't like them, so she married Danny instead. She and Danny think the choice was inspired. They grow daffodils in the sheltered elbows of The Gugh and give occasional visitors accommodation or cups of strong tea. They hope for snow in London or Manchester so that their golden flowers, delicately open in the mild Scilly air will fetch good prices.

Their island is like a recumbent cow. They have been preceded by primitive people centuries ago who left stone altars, elaborate graves and millions of mussel shells, dumped after eating.

Once the Scilly witches lived there, known as the Society of Skillful Aunts, remedying all ills, casting spells, and crowing at the moon. Ages before saw the early islanders prostrate at sunrise, bowed to the east, all around the single finger of stone that still stands on the downs and is called the Old Man of Gugh. Later there were resting pirates; wreckers, and those they wrecked; lovers who came by boat for solitude; and a solitary pioneering farmer who lies today under a grave of gorse and brambles on the forehead of the highest hill.

The two houses on The Gugh are a short field away from each other, their white faces looking out over the two fingers of ocean that touch, sometimes lovingly, sometimes roughly, across the sand bar at high tide. The houses are not pretty. They wear distinctly comical roofs, curved up like Napoleon's hat. But they are sturdy enough against storms and they have expansive expressions that smile at the evening going away over the final top of St. Agnes.

Danny and his wife, with Wendy's mother, live in one house and the other is kept for guests. Like all desert islanders they are never sure what time of day it is. "We keep a tag on summer and winter, mind," admitted Danny, "because of the flowers. But we're not too sure about the hours of the day. The only appointments we ever keep are with the launch and the tide."

Like castaways, too, they are ever hemmed in by domestic animals, cats, dogs and, of course, the donkey. They have a Chaplinesque spaniel whose daily daze is interrupted only when he walks into doors or falls spectacularly down the occasional flight of stairs. He's easy game for all the cats and once, when one of the other, wilder, household dogs was annoying Cuckoo it was he, idiotically innocent as ever, who got the donkey's kick.

It sent him through the air and rolling down on to the marran grass at the hem of the beach. He turned downcast eyes on the donkey and slunk away only to fall absently into the first rock pool.

On St. Agnes and The Gugh her little sister, the days slip into years hardly noticed. The storms from the belly of the ocean curl around the islands sometimes with shattering voice. But when they are spent and gone, the blue days come back and calm sea touches calm sky; the air is clear and salt, Danny calls from the tractor as it crosses the sand bar; Wendy waves from the door; the gulls shout; and Cuckoo pursues another dog. It is a good place.

Boats and Brothers

By eight o'clock the island is settled and the monks have doused the monastery lights, said their last lot of prayers, and have gone to bed. Evening is a good time to look at an island, anyway; from a distance, in quiet light, when it is still. Caldy, from the mainland, lies flat in the sea, its snout nosing out like the bill of a platypus. It has that animal's gently humped back too, and the beach facing the mainland could be its left paddler.

The summer sea was patterned with widespread folds, ribs and segments; its own mysterious geometry. Boats were gathered and tied until tomorrow in Tenby's harbour, and sitting among the others was the monks' boat, its fo'c'sle square and wooden, waiting to take me to Caldy.

They loaded it with bread and paraffin for the monks early next day and we set off, taking twenty minutes for the smooth leg of water. Sometimes in winter a south-east gale hoots along the coast and no one can touch Caldy for days.

There was a nun sitting by me on the cross-seat of the

monks' boat, an excited lady with shining spectacles and a
parted tooth. "It has an *atmosphere*," she affirmed. "No
doubt at all. Atmosphere! A man was running a mission
on the sands in Tenby last summer and not a soul bothered
with him. In the end he gave up trying to out-shout the
Punch and Judy and the little radios and took the boat over
to Caldy. There the people *listened* to him, the ordinary
visitors. They stood all around him and *listened* attentively.
It's the atmosphere, you see. He said it was well worth the
six shillings return."

The chugging boat came to the island, hugging tenta-
tively three wartime concrete invasion barges that never got
as far as a fight. They are Caldy's jetty, nose to tail, half
sunk in the sea, but breaking the awkward sweep of water
sometimes pushed against the island by the nor'-westers. A
ketch from Swansea used to beach here once a year and
Caldy's monks would unload 120 tons of coal from her,
enough to warm them through the year. They were black in
the face by the conclusion of their humping and the big
lumps were always toppling from the bags into their hanging
cowls as they waded through the cold surf.

"We used to pile it by the little cottage near the jetty,"
recalled Father Stephen, the Procurator of the Monastery.
"A couple of old ladies once came ashore here and I heard
one say to the other, 'Look at all that coal — just for one little
cottage.' We've got an electric cable now and we have
off-peak loading to heat the abbey. We need it too.
You try getting up at a quarter past two on a winter's
morning."

Father Stephen used to be a newspaper reporter in Leeds.
He's in his forties and he has taken the vow which means
he will remain on this island until he dies. He is quite content about it. When I first saw him he was sitting in the
little garden behind the coffee shop where the daily visitors
get their Nescafé and thick sandwiches. He has a thin,

strong face, not much hair, and a mild Yorkshire accent. He was wearing a blue boiler suit with wide flapping legs and a cowl, so that when he sat down it looked like a habit. It was a bit surprising to see him stride off—he has a purposeful, bandy walk, like a professional footballer—and to realise that what you imagined was a robe was, in fact, a very practical working outfit.

The old Norse sea-raiders, nosing out every hideout of the coasts, laid up at Caldy, dipping into its 'keld'—its freshwater spring—and giving it the name. The Welsh call it Ynys Pyr, Pyro's Island, after the holy hermit who lived there in prayer in the sixth century. He was the first settler. Pyro, the tyro, was followed by the Welsh saints, David, Illtud, Dyfrig and Gildas, and today the people of the island, and on the mainland too, would add the name of Father Thomas.

He was fifty-seven when he died, a man like a hill. A gentle, bull-necked monk, who used to drive the monastic amphibian, a wartime duck daubed bright yellow, across the racey channel to Tenby. To say simply that he was 'beloved' is to summon an ecclesiastical cliché, but it is nearest the truth. His cheerfulness and his sweetness, charity and faith, were matched only by his huge forgetfulness. He had been known to transport a shopping party of islanders to Tenby in his amphibian and then disappear for several days to some far part of Wales, leaving the melancholy shoppers waiting on the quay for the return journey. In Tenby the people are building a cliff-side arbour to be called Father Thomas's Garden. They thought that much of him.

Caldy's beach, the paddler of the platypus, is rimmed by a road all of four feet wide, along which the island tractor ridden by Charlie, a small grey man in a brown boiler suit, plunges from quay to village. Above the road hangs a hilly path, arched in places with thickly growing fuchsia, white hawthorns, a profuse raspberry-coloured weed beautiful as a genuine flower, and what looks suspiciously like elephant grass.

It is a cosy island, mild and sheltered by its own hump of little hills. Arum lilies stand like flags in the carp pool by the village green, and the walls of the row of coastguard cottages alongside are running wild with lovely flowers. Above the village there is a guest house of ecclesiastical grey stone with a soft lawn, a boat-shaped pool, and a low wall. On the wall are clutches of herbs and plants, thick, round and luxurious as sleeping cats. Poppies, bright and big, like tropic butterflies, move with the island breeze.

Isn't it strange how you always imagine monks to be old? The first monk I saw on Caldy was a teenager, striding noisily along the concrete road in white habit and shiny black boots. His hair was close cut, his ears stuck out, and his hands were thrust cheerfully into the front of his gown. He grinned and said: " 'Morning." He looked like a young soldier.

The thirty-five monks of Caldy keep pigs and make perfume to support themselves and their small abbey. The pigs have won almost as much renown — and more prizes — as the perfume. The brothers go out into the gorse and pick the flowers and there is a qualified chemist living in one of the coastguard cottages who supervises the blending of the perfume. They export it to America and it can be found in the smartest London shops. On the island you can buy it in a little green hut along with Caldy bath-essence, and aftershave lotion.

"Unfortunately," admitted the lady who serves it, "we have to check on each bottle as we sell it. The brothers are frequently called away to prayer and sometimes they have only half-filled a bottle and they forget to finish it when they get back."

The village green lies below the perfume works and the white abbey, in the deep of the bowl formed by Caldy's unambitious hills. It is faced by the island shop and post office, and a telephone box, whose metropolitan redness projects it brashly into the gentle scene. In 1939 there was one night of lashing storm and in the morning the abbot tried to ring the mainland and got only silence. They went to the seething beach and pulled a pathetic end of a cable out of the sea and that was the last of the telephone on Caldy until 1962 when they got the power cable across from Tenby. All messages, in between, went by morse lamp, which wasn't very private. The new telephone is better, everyone agrees. It's S.T.D. too.

The abbey, fringed by a beard of trees, sits on the hill above the village, wearing three small spires. Its walls are bright and white in the sun. Monks and lighthouse keepers must live in the world's best-painted buildings.

There is a signpost indicating the path to the abbey, adding the prim warning: 'Gentlemen Only'. It cuts alongside the file of coastguard cottages and, as I went by, a bulky woman in a black dress and flopping slippers came from one of the doors. She had a transistor radio slung around her neck in the manner a soldier carries his equipment. The plug from the radio was jammed uncompromisingly in her ear and she jogged to her own private music as she went out to empty her teapot. A robed monk came by carrying an electric power saw like a gun, and he and the lady wished each other a fine day.

The path rose and forked and I turned not into the abbey but to the midget church and its churchyard where old islanders and monks who kept their vow to remain for ever lie under their crosses. The church has a hole each side of its door into which a heavy beam was slotted to keep pirates and other nuisances out. The entire population would sit in the church until the intruders had gone home.

A broom and a pail stand beneath a brass plaque recalling William Bushell, Lord of the Manor of Caldy Island, and the church has other homely touches; two paraffin heaters to warm the worship on cold and early winter mornings.

Outside the June sun was lying in strips across the peaceful graves, its light serrated by screening trees. The bell in the abbey called, the monks left their work for prayer, and a jet fighter shattered the flat morning over the sea.

From the village the church and the abbey, a strong little road goes up the slope to the island's far side and the sturdy lighthouse. It thrusts through woods and weeds of almost tropical texture; copses and orchards bulge through hedges; there are nut trees, healthy young elderberries and more and wilder fuchsia.

A spindly track leaves the path and goes through the strange jungle, the warm air loaded with smells and excited insects. The elderberries have outgrown their strength, hand-shaped weeds and tangled flowers touch your shoulders. Half-hiding among it all, like some lost Amazon temple, is the rotting masonry of the Old Priory.

Follow the ruins and you emerge into a yard smelling fruitily of dung. The Priory, which since the Reformation has seen life as a malt-house, a forge, a barn, and a laundry, is now a farm.

Its worthwhile windows are protected by wire and its outbuildings are stuffed with great luxurious pigs. They lie and eat and grunt greatly, white and delicate pink, tended by the farm-monks; recognising the swish of a habit as the sign of food. The pig rearing is sophisticated and profitable. It's the brothers who lead the hard life.

The varied secular life of the Priory has, it is tempting to imagine, had a distressing effect on its spire. Worn smooth by the salt gales, weary of the years, it hangs full forty inches out of the perpendicular; possibly the only spire in the world to top a pig farm.

Higher than the Priory Farm the slim road goes between crops growing green in curved fields, and these fields are full of the summer song of hidden, anonymous birds. Obese thistles, the Scottish variety, eager to burst into purple, bank the flanks of the road. Then at the top is the cliff and the pounding sea. And the lighthouse.

How strong and how clean they are, these pillars of the coast. They set their kind faces to the oceans, patiently awaiting the assault of the wind, the slap of the sea, their shoulders squared and ready for the attack. But clean and white, walls brilliant, windows clear. Never a hair out of place.

Caldy's light works itself, throwing its message sixteen miles out to sea, white and red alternately, passing the nights in conversation with its brother, the Lundy light, across the waves to the south.

It has a splendid golden arrow shot through its cap, a weathervane, looking like the missile of some maritime William Tell. The cliffs are capped with slippery grass here, hanging in a casual fringe over the rocks. Seals lounge below, thick black seals, festooned across boulders, honking spectacularly, and raising their chins stylishly as the channel swell washes over them. There was a big one flat out across a single rock, lying like a man with a hangover, rolling a little to regain comfort after the passing of each disturbing wave. He gazed out to the world of blue-grey water, apparently decided it was all too much for him and closed his eyes for immediate sleep.

A seal family were busy in the waves just below me, jumping in and out as though a relative had fallen in and couldn't swim. Their heads bobbed comically from the water and they honked a lot. But the rest of the colony simply rested on the rocks, calling sometimes to reassure the others, but not bothering much beyond that.

There were gulls, of course, beating the blue sky, swooping against the rocky world, and making their lovely din. Their nests lie on the flat cliff-top, wedged, but only just, laid out, displayed, as though awaiting the judging in some contest, each with its cache of spotty brown eggs. The gulls did not mind my being there by the line of nests, in their street. They stood back without anxiety, each bird nodding an exquisite head as though indicating its own particular handiwork. I walked along, inspecting them all, but keeping my hands in my pockets. I did not want any misunderstandings. Their beaks are like chisels.

At one edge of that far Caldy cliff there is an abrupt drop and far below, a massive oblong of rock, corrugated like a terrace, strikes out into the surf. It is like a skyscraper which has fallen on its side.

Look south from there and Lundy Island is a bruise on the distant, fading sea. East is Worms Head, a finger of Wales, west is nothing but ocean currents. Turn north, away from the cliffs and the seals and you gaze down the smooth green back of Caldy to the tangled trees in the valley and the toy spires of the abbey. It was very solitary for a man up there in the June wind, on the cliff with the gulls and the sound of the sea. A thoughtful place.

I stood, still as the lighthouse, and heard a booming voice. My mood told me it was the Voice of God, but it wasn't. Below, around the corner of the sea came a bright boat from Tenby, thick with trippers and a man with a megaphone drawing attention to the seals in the surf. Disappointing.

On the patch of green by the coastguard cottages I found Father Stephen. Some day visitors had just come ashore and two boys were kicking a red football across the grass.

"I suppose you could say that a man who comes here to stay sacrifices a lot," nodded the monk. "But I looked at the world after the war and I knew that I needed something it could not give me. I've found it here on this island."

The boat trippers were exploring their sandwiches, sitting on the stone toadstool seats by the green. Father Stephen laughed. "We are vegetarians," he said. "No meat, no fish, nor anything like that. But we let the novices have an egg for their midday meal. We had a French brother here once who was more or less pressed into being the abbey cook. He was not very good and even a monk's patience gets stretched sometimes. The food got worse and worse, and one day as I was going past the kitchen window I heard our French brother bellowing about in a most untoward way. Then a cookery book flew through the window and I heard him shout: 'Get out, Madam Beaton, get out!' "

Father Stephen went off busily, the curious blue boiler-suit flapping at the ankles as he walked his footballer's walk. I took the path to the abbey now, through creeks of sunlight coming between the close trees, along the paved paths and between the profuse flowers.

"We are trying out some new chants," said the monk who took me around the abbey. "For a long time we have used the Gregorian Chant in our services, but we are experimenting with some modern chants. Some of them are quite painful, I'm afraid, but in twenty or thirty years we think we may have a nice chant to suit everybody."

His name was Father Senan; a boney face, close-haired, a delicate humour in his eye and speech. He was once a doctor. He mentioned that there was a doctor on the island and that if anyone was sick they could be taken off by helicopter. He did not say that he was the doctor.

We were in the abbey church when he talked of the chants, fingering the bulky leather books that sit stonily above each monk's stall. It is a coldly plain building, in keeping with the way of the Cistercian Order, with a lovely, awesome, acid green light on the altar set in the far archway.

Our Lady, cast in concrete, hovers above the arch and the roof, rebuilt after it burned down when a fuse blew in 1939, is fine, simple, wood buttressing.

From the cool church along a cloistered walk we went,

bounding a grassed courtyard dominated by a statue of Jesus and a big black water tank. More archways and then we stood in the refectory, a scrubbed, hollow place, with each brother's meal place laid with his plate, his cutlery and his jug of water. Along the board tables were bowls of salad and vegetables.

Father Senan nodded at a little pulpit jutting from the wall. "During our meals one of the brothers reads to us from some religious book, and then a few passages from something else, perhaps travel or biography," he said. "Recently too we've been listening to tape recordings of music during our meals." He hesitated, then said: "Only the classics of course. Nothing wild."

The library was next, with a desk for each monk, and its reading material — *The Life of St. Bernard*, *A History of the English Speaking Peoples*, and *Farming Through the Year*. On the newspaper table the *Guardian*, the *Farmer and Stockbreeder* and the *Catholic Herald*.

We went into the sunlight again. "Our novices," said the monk nodding at a low prefabricated building behind the abbey. "That's where they live. It used to be a synagogue in a wartime Jewish refugee camp. It's come in very useful for us."

I went from the abbey, across the patchwork green and its coastguard cottages ringed with flowers, and through the fuchsias towards the jetty. On the forehead of the rise from the brilliant gorse I could see across the channel, placid to Tenby, the oblong hotels and boarding houses of the town standing up like waiting luggage. A boat was making a seam across the sea, heading for Caldy and coming for me.

Along the path plodded two day-visitors, Yorkshire people, middle-aged, the solid woman in her flowered dress, and her husband, smaller, in his open-necked shirt and sandals. She was talking about the monks. . . .

"They coom 'ere," she boomed, "for the love of God." She paused and puffed. "And," she wagged her finger at him, "because they're tired and sick of the world."

He glanced up from the height of her shoulder, made a screwed-up face, and added: "Aye, and women."

A Place for Puffins

We went south from Gutness, on the tail of Shetland; three hours for twenty-three miles in a tubby fishing boat, barging, dancing, rolling across The Roost. We seemed to fix on the exact seam where the Atlantic and the North Sea meet and don't take to each other. One ocean buffeted us, the other rolled us and threw us back at the first. It was July.

Acres of pallid blue sky kept coming from the horizon, then dun patches and spiteful rain. Puffins, buzzing rather than flying, went across the waves in handfuls, cormorants did acrobats for fish, and some other sea-bird, tight and neat as a well-wrapped parcel, sat on the great waves and looked at our poor pitching boat with concern.

If there was consolation, and you need some in a sea like that at mid-summer when you might easily be paddling at Worthing or swimming in the Aegean, it was that the island was always visible. Just ahead, waiting, sitting still upon the sea. Fair Isle.

They call the little boat *The Good Shepherd* and the

islanders never refer to her in any other manner, abbreviation or nickname. She makes the trip to Gutness on Tuesdays and Fridays in summer and once a week in winter. Only once having set out has she ever had to turn back and then the storm was so bad everyone knew she could never have lived in it. Sometimes in winter the Fair Isle sailors, who all have the good name of Stout, look at the waves and the weather and decide not to make the trip to Shetland, but their little island has never been isolated for more than two weeks. They are superb seamen and very brave.

On that bumpy summer morning Jerry Stout, the captain, Tommy Stout, George Stout and Teddy Stout, his crew, were enjoying what was for them an easy run. They watched a fishery protection cruiser moving cleanly along the eastern edge of the horizon and wondered if she would apprehend the lobster poachers fishing that moment on the far side of their island. On the mad deck we sickly passengers hunched between the deck cargo. A sturdy young Ministry of Works man, green to the ears, kept a duty eye on the piled pieces of a coastguard shed he was escorting. It slipped and slithered on the forward hatch and the Ministry man gallantly went forward to secure it with more rope. Whitehall would have been proud.

But the island, like a steely promise, was always just ahead, huge and already magical, thrusting strong and high, clear of anything the sea could throw or threaten. At ten miles, when one of the wandering patches of open sky was above it, and viewed at intervals when the bow of the boat was thrown down not up, it showed itself as one big hump with a minor hump hanging on to its tail. But gently and gradually as we closed towards North Haven, its sheltered landfall, the sweet upland greens showed in the sun, and the hills and rocks took on shapes and contours. Then the squares of a few buildings, the noble head of a lighthouse, the movement of birds across the cliff faces, and the white

embroidery of more birds sitting in thousands on the dark
ledges.

It is this delicate opening up of any and every island as
you come from the sea that is such a glad experience, that
lifts the eyes and sharpens the anticipation, that makes the
most reluctant sailor glad he sailed and arrived at such a
place.

It is the soaring slab of Sheep Craig, the little hump of the
distant viewer, now grown and close, that holds the gaze
when you sail into the locked waters of North Haven. It
jumps athletically straight to the sky in the background,
sloping, spectacular, sliced down and covered green with
fine pasture.

It must be the nearest thing in the world to a vertical
meadow and the sheep that feed on it for the whole wild
winter and the uncertain summer must develop shelving
hoofs. The sun was bright on its green shoulder as we
went to the little jetty, and the whole sky was busy with
birds.

They say the name Fair Isle comes either from the Gaelic
Fear An — Far Island — or the Norse Fridarey — Sheep Isle.
To see the maritime blue eyes and the Viking fairness of the
Fair Isle men and their children is to know the true answer
immediately. But today it is more an isle of birds than of
sheep. The lucky fliers, weary on their migratory voyages,
find this rocky landfall and stay and sleep. The sea birds
nest while others rest. Strident gulls, fulmers, oyster-
catchers, outshout the waves, and on the grassy upland
places the song is sweet and piping. On this spot, three by
one-and-a-half miles, half the birds of Europe hold family
gatherings. Bird-watchers lie in the covering heather and
risk their necks on rocky ledges every hour, observing loves,
lives, deaths and departures. As you sail into North Haven
there is an islet squatting in the centre of the channel topped
by a box-like bird hide made of sacking by some enthusiast.

A huge herring gull was peeping quizzically into the hole, observing in reverse, as we went by in our boat.

* * *

At night the birds go quiet, but the sea is louder, the wind steps up its note, and the seals join a ghostly chorale in the Fair Isle caves. It is at once enchanting and hideously melodic. They sing with or against the wind and the waves as the mood takes them. When there is moonlight and it shines on the patchy sea for miles, and finds its way into the seals' caves they sing more heartbreakingly than ever.

Night at the bird observatory, the geometrical assortment of former navy huts on the beach at North Haven, is a time for cocoa and stories. There is always a fire, and you feel grateful for its warmth and its inherent sense of security in that wild corner of the sea.

The talk is almost always of boats and birds. They are the everyday things of Fair Isle, the most important topics, the interest and the livelihood of all the people are bound up in them. Every islander is a bird-watcher, reporting anything strange seen or heard, every bird-watcher is an islander, even if only for a while. The boats, more particularly *the* boat — *The Good Shepherd* — and the concern of everyone. Without them they could not live. Fads and fashions, pavements and politics, are miles away and of no matter. The singing of the seals is real.

"Years ago," related Roy Dennis, the warden of the observatory, a black-haired young man, emerging from his cocoa mug. "Years ago there was a small boat here called the *Columbine*. Two brothers owned her and one day they undertook to take an elderly crippled woman to Lerwick so she could have some treatment. She was in a wheel-chair and couldn't be taken out of it. So they secured the chair on the *Columbine's* deck, tied it to the mast and set off with the old lady fixed like that.

"It was a good sort of day with a trace of breeze and they were sailing along quite well when one of the brothers saw something in the water—a big lump of driftwood or such-like—and decided to get it. He took the dinghy over to it, but managed to lose one of the oars while he was trying to get the wood from the water. His brother, seeing the valuable oar floating away, jumped into the sea, swam to it and took it across to the dinghy. No sooner was he overboard than a puff of wind came up from nowhere and set the *Columbine*, with the old girl stuck in her wheel-chair on deck, off across the water.

"The brothers rowed like mad but they couldn't catch the sailing boat and eventually the cries of the old lady faded and the boat went out of sight. The *Columbine* travelled miles until some Norwegian fishermen, unbelievingly, found her sailing along with the old dear still in her wheel-chair and still yelling. . . ."

In summer night comes late, hardly drawing its curtains before the northern dawn pulls them brilliantly open again. One dusty evening, about ten, all the fifty people went to the community centre, a low and stony place sitting across the brown field from the chapel, to see a film of the Queen's visit to their isle. They laughed when they saw themselves on the screen and clapped patriotically as though she could hear, when Her Majesty mounted the Fair Isle lorry, scrubbed and rubbed clean for her, to be borne on her tour.

After the film there were formation dances and reels to a fiddle, an accordion, and a guitar, everyone thumping and raising the dust under paper decorations and shrivelled balloons, remnants of far-off Christmas. Only tea and cakes were served, for the Fair Islander keeps his bottle in a dark cupboard and doesn't often take it out. Young Anne and Stewart Thomson, whose father is the postmaster, sang:

Far away across the waters
Lies the dear land of our birth. . . .
And no heart could 'ere forget
Our one beloved island home.

Outside, when the dancing had stopped at midnight, it was still twilight, the south lighthouse turning its fair light, the waves still clear against the dark head-and-shoulder rocks offshore. Sheep stirred in the bronze fields and the young people from the dance went, some walking, some running, happy, hand in hand across the tired daylight, over the heather to the crofts spread out on the low hills. Parents took children along the road, their voices and laughter flying clear to us who remained by the stone chapel waiting for the light to go.

It is easy in this soft place, this mannered island, to realise how the years must arrive and depart almost without notice, from childhood until it is time to die. The Christmas decorations and the balloons like shrivelled fruit at the dance bothered no one's sense of duty or time. One mile away, flung across the side of a hill of sprightly moss and grass, lies the still-shiny tail and part of the fuselage of a German aeroplane. It's been there, in wind and sun, for a quarter of a century, but no one has yet swept up the litter. The tail is jammed in a ditch and the fractured body sticks up like a metallic tree stump. On the higher, more open ground, are the engines, solid with rust, and all the fragments of that war night when two enemies died and two were taken prisoner by the Fair Isle men.

There can be few places where such a relic remains without causing the least concern or conscience. The two dead airmen were buried in the island cemetery alongside shipwrecked sailors and mouldering coastguards. After the war the Germans sent a mission to Fair Isle and the bodies were taken out and carried back to Germany. The two Germans taken prisoner on that distant night of adventure were kept by the islanders until the R.A.F. sent a launch from Sumbrugh, Shetland, to claim them. To the intense interest of the assembled island the airmen managed to wreck their launch on the rocks at North Haven and arrived ashore wet and humiliated to wait, with their captives, until the lifeboat came to fetch them from Lerwick.

The Fair Isle churchyard is a mile, beyond two small hills, from both the church and the chapel. When someone dies it is a long, bleak walk for the people who carry the coffin and those who follow, especially in the dark wind of winter. The graveyard is shaggy with marran grass and bends over from the land towards the biting sea, as though to let the dead see the waves. The Stouts are all there, from way back, of course, and the Wilsons and the Thompsons.

As for all island men it was the sea, their beautiful friend, their unlovely enemy, which claimed many of them. Drowning is a natural death on Fair Isle.

Seventy years ago they used to go out in their spindly sixerns, tough two-man boats, venturing for fish far out towards Norway. They used to light a little open fire amidships to warm them and give them hope and hold them through the ocean nights. When they had a full catch they would row for North Haven, let the women gut the fish, then row to Gutness to sell some of it to the great Laird at his price. Then back to Fair Isle they would make, pick up the rest of the catch and take it to Orkney, thirty miles away, for a better belly-filling price on the unofficial market. And all this in a day and a night.

But the thin boats were easy pickings for a storm. Sometimes the rowers pulled back through the great roughs and troughs and reached the haven, and sometimes they could not achieve it. When the sea was calm again their folk searched for their bodies, sang over them, and carried them to the shaggy patch of grass near the southern cliffs where they lie today.

* * *

There are so many people called Stout on Fair Isle that the name has dispensed with itself. A man and his wife are known to all by the name of their croft. There is Mires Jerry, School Jimmy, Utra Jerry and Leogh Willy, who is a former coastguard and knows every cave, hole, gully and rock of the curling shore. Then there is Mrs. Busta, whose true name is Helen Stout, and Utra Lottie and Utra Helen, and Mrs. Midway Stout.

"We knew a time," said Mrs. Busta, "when only the needles of a few women kept families on Fair Isle from starvation. The fishing failed and there was not enough from the land, and we would sit and knit these old patterns and send them to the mainland for food or whatever they liked to give us in return. And sometimes it wasn't very much."

She and Molly Wilson sat in the community centre, rather splendid beneath the decorations and wrinkled balloons, with gloves and scarves and jumpers, worked in the rare, square Fair Isle stitch, spread before them on a collapsible card-table.

Each Monday they meet, a self-appointed examining committee, with Utra Lottie as a third member, to press their eyes and noses close along the intricate stitches of the garments made by eight knitters on the island.

When each piece of work has been touched, tested and talked about, it is, if it passes, given a silk Fair Isle label. Today they go to only private customers. You never see them in the shops; not even the smartest.

"We know they are good stuff," said Mrs. Busta. "We've had jumpers back for repair after forty years because the sleeves have worn. Women in Shetland and other places have tried to copy the work of Fair Isle but they don't know our secrets. We keep them very close, you understand."

When the Armada made its odd northward flight after defeat at the guns of Drake's sailors, it left wrecks and men on many cunning rocks and little isles about the coast. One galleon, *El Gran Grifon*, collided with Fair Isle in the dark and all the Spaniards gained the shore. There they remained for a long time, making friends, fathering children, and eating the islanders to the edge of famine. They eventually left when there was scarcely a crust left in any croft cupboard, but, so the Fair Isle women say today, they left, in exchange, the marvellous secret of the dyes which have since been used to make the soft colours used in the island knitting.

"It takes one woman two weeks to knit a Fair Isle sweater," said Mrs. Busta. "In the winter, when it's dark at three in the day, or earlier, we sit in and knit by the peat fires." She picked up a cheerful blue and white hat. "We used to call these night-caps," she smiled. "Old men used to wear them in bed. Now they're called ski-caps. We have a lot of orders for them."

"Once a year," said Molly Wilson, "we go out and get the flowers and the plants we need and we make the dyes, boiling them up in one of the crofts. We never let anybody see how they are made. One boil-up is enough for that year. When women die on Fair Isle they always make sure that somebody else knows how to make the mixture."

"When we were girls, you know," said Mrs. Busta, running her thin fingers along one of the knitted patterns, "all of us had a mind to leave the island. We wanted to see all the world. But not now. I've been — mind you — down to England. But I didn't like all the trees and I was homesick for the sea."

*　　*　　*

Most of the people live in the crofts spread wide across

the south of the island where the land is easier for tilling and growing and the sheep graze better. There is no village in the normal meaning, no close living. The stony track they call the road goes in that direction from North Haven, passing the stricken aeroplane on its left and the island's optimistic airstrip among the heather, and the nesting gulls on the right.

"The winds are too strong," any islander will say when you mention aeroplanes. "Half the time they'd never get them down."

The island nurse, Una Stout, a go-ahead young woman, would be glad of a helicopter. She was striding towards the crofts on the sea-edge when I saw her, her small son jumping in and out of the heather by the way. "My best argument for a helicopter," she said, "is a couple of winter trips by that so-and-so *Good Shepherd*. If you're trying to look after a patient and being sick over the side at the same time you consider that there must be other ways of doing it."

But others shake their heads. No helicopter either, they say. "The *Good Shepherd*," an old man said patiently, "carries us and everything to do with our life here. That includes Her Majesty's Mail. And we get a subsidy for Her Majesty's Mail."

Below the airstrip, enveloped in deep folds and fissures of the land, fed by a copious stream that spreads itself among reeds and rushes, are the Fair Isle trees. The airstrip just has the edge on them as the island's most optimistic project. They are the thorniest conifers, planted years ago, and now attaining a maximum height of three-feet six. There are children on the island who have never seen a real tree, nor a policeman in uniform. Every so often the five children at the school have a special treat — an outing to see how big the trees have grown. Birds, flying long and lone migrations, are unlikely to find any support or solace among their branches for many years.

Cuckoo patrolling his beach

St. Agnes lighthouse

*Fair Isle's only
link with the rest
of the world—*
The Good
Shepherd. *Sheep
Rock is in the
background*

Amphibian monks. The Duck amphibious craft used by the Cistercian brothers on Caldy Island

The 25-year-old wreck of the German aeroplane

John Dennison aboard The Fairy Queen

Winter seas around the South Light, Fair Isle

On Auskerry John Dennison tries to save the drowned sheep with the kiss of life

The baldness of the inner landscape of the island, the naked, mildly curved hills, stretching out, gives way abruptly to the static violence of cliffs. High, by itself like a white toy, on one of the brown rises, where the winds of winter must hit it hard, is the kirk. There is nothing to break the sleeping barren smoothness of the horizon on either side. It stands like a small but urgent summons and all the people go to worship there each Sunday morning. In the evening they all go to the non-conformist chapel. There are not enough islanders to quibble about denominations and everybody thinks the arrangement is fine. Every Christmas there are two church socials and everyone goes to them too.

But let a parson, any parson, travel in *The Good Shepherd* —despite its appellation—and the sailors grumble and frown. He's bad luck in a boat. It has to be thoroughly washed out afterwards. He is almost as much bad luck as a pig. He's never mentioned by name. They just call him 'The Upstander'. Everybody is glad when he has taken his bags and gone ashore.

"We've got a few funny ideas," admitted Mrs. Busta Stout. "Superstitions and such things. When I was a girl the men believed it was bad luck if any of them saw their wives on the road when they were walking to the boat to go fishing. I've known the time when it's happened and all the men have turned about and gone home again. Nor would they move from their fires that day."

On the lumpy road the Fair Islanders have established a little signpost, eighteen inches high, with pieces of thin stick pointing in various directions and carrying the words: 'Schoolhouse', 'Church', 'Store' and others. It is of use only to the newest of arrivals because after one walk, on one morning, it is impossible not to know where everything is.

Stewart Wilson keeps the store. He is the classic Fair Islander, a straight line from the Scandinavians; short, sturdy, bright fair hair and jumping blue eyes. His fifteen-month-old son Stephen looks the same.

"Centuries ago," he said, "we were traded, with the Shetlands and the Orkneys as part of a wedding dowry given by the King of Norway, who wanted to get his daughter married off to James the First of Scotland. But somehow we've never become Scots. Some Government official in London once put up a bonus for a Gaelic-speaking teacher to come up to the isles. He got his facts a bit wrong. Nobody up here speaks Gaelic. He was thinking about the Western Isles."

His whitewashed store, with its cosy inner living-room sells everything from soap-powders to gramophone records. When he is not serving behind the counter he is taking splendid photographs of a peach-coloured dawn swimming over Sheep Craig, or training the kirk-chapel choir for a musical evening.

Sheila Wilson, his wife, is pale and quiet. She is from Kent and she has lived in London. "I never miss it for a second," she said. "People *care* about you here, and you find yourself caring about them. You could never find this in a city. It's a good feeling, unique in little places like this. We have a full life, so full I never know where the days or the hours go. We can get television here, you know. We're not *that* isolated. But there aren't very many sets. People are so busy."

*　　*　　*

From the stubby jetty at North Haven a rocky paw of Fair Isle reaches out to the east. This is where the seals are; where the birds gather in wondrous congregations; where the baby rabbits scramble and bounce through the springy grass.

Here the rocks fall in gigantic blades, cutting into the perfect texture of the sea, riling it and throwing it up in white annoyance.

Walking up there, in the mild sun of the northern summer, I roused the panicky oyster-catchers into a frenzy of flying and crying as though they had taken it upon themselves to warn the entire coast of my invasion. Black and white, orange-beaked, they flash about in awful terror. Or so you think, until you realise that this is how they always are. They shout even when they have nothing to shout about; when they do have an excuse then it's twice as loud.

The sheep, clipping the spongy grass, looked up as I came walking against the wind, and, having moved a statutory eighteen inches the other way, continued eating. One night, not long ago, one of the Fair Isle men found an ewe bleating on a ledge half-way down one of these cliffs. There was half-an-inch between the animal and a long drop. The man got a rope, went down, and found the rope was too short. But only by a bit, so he tried it anyway. He hung on to the rope with one hand and tried to get hold of the sheep with the other. The adventure ended with man and sheep stuck on the ledge, the man injured and unable to move.

When night came on the other island men went to look for their neighbour. Twelve of them, with a pocket torch, got him up that blank cliff in a raging wind. And the sheep too. They each got a certificate from the Carnegie Hero Trust, and £100 between them. They put the money towards getting electricity for Fair Isle.

I walked carefully out along one of the slim peninsulas of black rock. The grass thrust itself out a good distance, apparently sustained on nothing, and there was thrift, the lovely, delicate sea-pink, growing in any place where there was a little earth to keep it. The rocks were warm in the sun, the sea shining and spread like rolled steel, uninterrupted to its meeting with the sky.

With care I selected a wide cleft and wedged myself in it, flat on my back, with thick sweater and anorak keeping out the wind. The sky was as limitless as the sea, but busier;

constantly riven with birds. The still-squeaking oyster-catcher, the little ringed plover, the gull in every variety; kittiwakes, shearwaters, skuas who will attack a man, fulmers who, they say, will rise above a storm and sleep peacefully in the sky, head below wing, until it is all over.

Seals, half a dozen jet heads, trod water a few waves off the rocks; cormorants did their acrobatics for fish. On a slope of grass below me sat thirty puffins, like a Welsh male voice choir mildly dazed after a beery outing. On a shelf under the puffins half a dozen black shag stood mournfully, shifting uneasily, as though waiting the arrival of an acquaintance in a coffin.

From my ledge I could see clearly the sheep clinging to the rearing hump of Sheep Craig. Once a year, in September, the men row out to the base of this great toadstool of rock and grass and climb the chain that takes them to the sloping summit. They go up to shear the sheep, drink beer, and then inch down again, lowering any sheep who have to be taken back to the main island. It's hard and hazardous, but the men say that the pasture on Sheep Craig is thicker and richer than on any part of Fair Isle. The women say the men go for the day's outing.

The chain they ascend to that strange listing pasture came from an immigrant ship wrecked many years ago. It's not difficult to catch the sheep because they cannot run far. The men take the wool, lower a couple of the oldest sheep inhabitants into the boat below, drink the beer, and leave by late afternoon. The flock, feeling that night a mite chilly, begins another year's uninterrupted grazing. Life has few excitements on Sheep Craig.

I dozed in the mild sun. The oyster-catchers, like news-paper sellers shouting some sensation, woke me. The puffins were still there, observing the funereal shag. Some baby rabbits blinked at the puffins. The sea was ruffled now with the beginnings of a breeze. There was a ship square and distinct against the pale horizon. I was stiff from lying across the rock, so I got up and cat-walked along the blades of rock. Day-old gulls, handfuls of dusty fluff, wedged themselves in the fissures and hoped I would not notice. There were clutches of eggs too, pillowed on meagre grass, brown splashed, some being opened industriously from the inside by the birds ready for the blowy world.

An eider duck, brown and fat, squatted like a dowager, never moving an eye nor shifting an inch on her eggs as I crouched by her. Roy Dennis told me she came back to the same spot every year. "We ringed her on the first season," he grinned. "Now every year when we find her again, still in the same place, she just sticks her leg over the side of the nest so we can see the ring. Then she tucks it under again and carries on looking into space. She's a good duck, that one."

* * *

I made the last day on Fair Isle stretch a long time. It had been squally early on, with the sea looking needled. But it died and settled into a fine, pale summer's day. Every sort of bird was singing or calling that day. There were hundreds of puffins on the slippery grass overlooking North Haven, and rabbits scampering white and brown; a curl of smoke wandered up from the huts of the bird observatory; *The Good Shepherd* sat bright in the flat waters of the haven and the Stout brothers worked on painting the slipway where they would haul her during the wanton winter days to come.

Some visitors had come ashore and on the road one of them was admiring the sweater which Roy Dennis's small son was wearing.

"Fair Isle, isn't it?" she asked the boy's mother.

"Marks & Spencer's," said Marina Dennis.

I borrowed an aged bicycle, almost spokeless and entirely brakeless, to ride over to the crofts. The road was no smoother, but the air was free and clean. In the village they were laughing about a story the Stout boys had brought back from Lerwick. A Norwegian fisherman had been staggering down the main street, a couple of nights before, brimming with scotch, and had seen an accordion in a shop window. Joyfully he smashed the window and went down the road playing the squeezebox. The police had no trouble in tracing him.

Sheila Wilson gave me some tea and I started back for North Haven on my bicycle in the bright afternoon. There were sheep being driven for early shearing along the green cliff-grass by the lighthouse. The crofts and the island fields were quiet otherwise. On their separated hills, like twin virtues, the kirk and the chapel sat. In the middle of the flat land between the road and the cliffs stood a ruined croft, roofless, looking strangely like a high-backed chair. Where the road topped the hill Nurse Una Stout walked briskly, holding the hand of her tugging boy. I began to pedal.

So full was I of the sights and the lovely feeling of Fair Isle, so sad that it was time to leave, that I forgot there were no brakes on the bike. Down one stony slope I travelled, then another. The placid scenery began to quicken and then to shoot past at a fearful rate, like a film gone mad. I couldn't stop it. It was running away with me. I was a panic-held boy again. Years ago. Help!

As I careered I shouted. First to Nurse Una and the boy. "Look out! Out of the way. I can't stop!"

Una pulled the lad into the hedge and I whizzed on, a ghastly grin tacked to my face. Then another hill . . . and another bend . . .

Around the bend came the island Land-rover. In a place boasting of three motor vehicles I was about to become the first road casualty. There was no room for two of us. I twisted the handlebars and flung the bike into a brambled ditch, flying on and landing spectacularly head first in an earthy rabbit warren.

It was a brilliant crash. As I turned over and lay there I could hear Nurse Una calling that she was coming to help. The Land-rover stopped and the men came back. Even before they got there to join me I was laughing. Laughing loud with huge happiness. Because I had not fallen from a bike in too many years, because the sky was spotless above my head, and because the birds sang and the grass and the heather smelled so fine. Because life was good and people cared.

Because this was an island.

4 AUSKERRY

Shearing Saturday

She fidgeted alongside the quay at Stronsay in the Orkneys. Forty-three feet of hard, salted timber, the smell of fish about her, tackle on the deck, the wheelhouse windows brined up, and stuck to them a coloured sticker advertising a 'Great Competition! Golden Wonder Crisps'.

"It's just a joke," said John Dennison, her skipper. "I stuck it up there one day for a laugh and now I can't get it off. Looks a bit funny, doesn't it."

He was a carefully spoken man, his Orkney accent quiet and curiously Welsh. He looked as though the wind hit him in the face a lot and had perhaps blown out a couple of teeth. Their absence made his grin more exotic. He was tubby and strong, like his boat.

"God knows why we call her *The Fairy Queen*," he said, thick legs astride on the boards. We were waiting for the sheep-shearers to arrive. There was a punchy sort of wind coming in through the islands and the sea was all lumps. Sometimes, briefly, the sun came out and caught the backs of the waves, making them seem no more friendly.

"More like a Fairy Cow, sometimes," he went on, squinting up the wooded length of her with perverse affection. "I'm getting a new one soon. Steel hulled and bigger. Then I can fish and to hell with the weather. I can't do that now."

He was a full, remarkable man. When I walked into his pub on Stronsay, the only one on the island, he was working the beer handles. He had been out fishing for skate for two rowdy nights, landed his catch at Wick, collected his money, and got back to Stronsay in time to open the saloon bar. He turned out to be the assistant coxswain of the lifeboat as well—and a farmer, a part-time lighthouse keeper, a piper in the pipe band, a fiddler in the Northern Lights Dance Orchestra, a reader, a wit and a philosopher of the sea. He also took the photographs at local weddings and developed them when he had the time. This meant, he said, that the couple sometimes had kids before they actually got the prints.

"I've got a wee island," he had mentioned, wiping his way through a pile of beer glasses. "Auskerry—nine miles south, just about. There's no one there, it's just sheep and birds and the sea. Some o' the boys are going across tomorrow to shear the sheep." He laughed. "And I'll have to put a drop of oil in the lighthouse too. I fancied I heard it squeaking last night."

So we were by the jetty the next day. July in Orkney can be clear and gold, but a niggling wind was up and frightened clouds ran before it over the open places between the flung islands. The three Dennison lads came along the jetty, in correct order, Magnus, tall, assured, quiet, a fisherman at seventeen, then Roy, a year his junior, waiting to finish school and wanting to fish too, and Keith, twelve, smiling behind his spectacles. He confessed that the sea sometimes made him throw up.

There was a sheepdog, predictably Lassie, and then the other men, Ray, Dave Cooper with the rusty hair, Jackie, his brother, Norman in the scarlet shirt, Francis, with his red tammy and Colin in his grey one; Robbie 'O'Gesty' Miller, and John 'O'Kirbuster' Stevenson — named from the places they farmed.

We pushed off, hugged the hind of Stronsay for a while, then made a cut across the open sea. Brittle rain rapped the wheelhouse window, and the sea came up and slapped us like a boxer hitting with an open glove. "A shower," sniffed John Dennison, although he said it 'shooer'. "No more, I'll be hoping. Can't shear wet wool. We might as well go home."

The rain thinned and stopped, but the wind still skidded into the ploughing boat, and the sun that came out was bright and without feeling. Magnus came into the wheelhouse, opened a diminutive trap door and slithered into the oily space where the engine laboured. The men sat on the deck, shaking the rain off their shoulders, their hats and their heads. One of them stumbled towards the wheelhouse, across the bucking boat, bent forward first, and then back. He seemed to have something urgent to say. The wheelhouse door was wrenched open and the wind threw itself in.

"John," said the man apologetically. "I'm hoping to be back for eight tonight. Will we be back?"

"Aye, sure," said John, almost absently pulling the wheel to starboard. "We'll be back. No worry." The man went out and the wind went with him.

"He'll be wanting to watch the telly," said the skipper. "There's nowhere else he would be wanting to go on Stronsay on Saturday night at any special time."

He laughed quietly. Gulls were gyrating about the boat as though they were on wires fixed to the mast. Big floppy waves came over the side at intervals, like wet hands trying to get a grip on the bulwarks.

The island was before us now, low and flat, green, bedded on white surf, its lighthouse like a superior feather.

"Auskerry," announced John, then, changing the subject. "One day we're going to sail to Norway. We're always talking about it, but we've never got to doin' it. Maybe when we get the new boat. The good, big one with the steel hull."

We came close in, running between small toothy skerries, through jumbled currents, peered at by sheep looking over the lip of the low cliffs. "We'll make for the geo with the pier," said John, probably talking to himself. "The wee inlets are called geos," he said to me over his shoulder. He began turning the radio dials. "We'll get the forecast," he said.

The B.B.C. news was on, a firm urban voice informing us on the war in Vietnam, the death of a famous actress, what the Home Secretary said in Parliament. It came to us out there in the grey and bumpy sea, alongside an uninhabited island, with the smell of oil and fish in my nose, and the whirring of seabirds in my eyes, and it seemed something unreal and unimportant.

John slewed the boat between two murderous sets of skerries, and made for the inlet by the lighthouse. "I used to like her," he said, meaning the famous actress, now dead. "Ready boys? We're going in on this one."

*   *   *

The island was low, grass and gorse covered, pimpled with occasional rashes of rock, and canopied by gulls and other seabirds. All the rainclouds had gone over the further islands and the distant sea, and the white wings above us beat against a pale, clean sky.

They got the boat, rearing at the nose, into the sharp sheltered inlet, the geo, and the boys and the men and the excited dog all jumped down, timing their leaps with the ebbing of the sea across the flat rocks. I walked up the fissure after them. They were laughing among themselves, carrying the shearing tools, and the beer, uncomplicated men, quiet as strong men can afford to be quiet, ready to do a day's sweating work, hoping to be home across the sea again in time for television at eight.

"Eighty-three, eighty-four, seventy-seven," I heard John Dennison recite. I knew he was talking about the total of new lambs for the past three seasons. He had the numbers cut into the woodwork inside the wheelhouse of his boat.

We reached the mossy top of the cliff passage, just below the lighthouse. "I'll get the key for you," said John. "You might as well see all of Auskerry at one go. We'll be busy a wee while, rounding up the sheep."

He got the key and opened the front door of the lighthouse. I went up. It was like being in a tipped-up tunnel; steep curling stairs, the clanging echo of every footstep taken, a strange sort of purified sea-scent, and a childhood sensation of excitement that you thought was lost long years before.

There was a narrow room almost at the summit, just under the light. It had a little desk and a high stool, a couple of pencils and some books. How strange it must have been for the lighthouse keeper to have sat at his desk, so high up there, on a night of violent winter weather, at that lone northern island. Working at his books and his tide tables, perched up there in the uncouth storm, while above him the saving light whirled quietly, and far away in cities people sat in restaurants and theatres.

Pinned to the wall beside the desk was an impressive Notice to Mariners, issued when the lighthouse keepers left Auskerry and the light began its solitary, automatic, function, its only regular visitor the faithful John Dennison.

The Commissioners for the Northern Lights, that almost celestial body by the sound of them, gave warning that

Auskerry Lighthouse, Latitude 59.01 N., Longitude 2.34 W., flashing every 20 seconds for 0.5 seconds with a 67,000 Candlepower, was to be unmanned, said the notice. Beneath it leaned a chunky book, containing the names of all the lighthouse keepers over the fair and stormy years, some pens and ink, and a broom for sweeping up. Going down into that little room must have been like finding a cave of comfort for a keeper who had been up in the light itself on a lashing midnight. I expect he made his cocoa there.

There was a strong central column, smooth and fine, like the periscope in a submarine, thrusting up through the ceiling to carry the light. There was a steel ladder going up terminating in a trap door bolted on each side. I climbed and slipped the bolts, pushing up the heavy trap with my head, then my shoulders, levering it back, and then stepping up and out into the wonderful glass globe of the lighthouse.

The light itself sat majestically as some island god, balanced beautifully at its centre, every piece clean and strong metal, looking out over the restive sea, blue in the sun, while the big birds flapped at its windows.

Through the windows the sun streamed hot and magnified. There was a slim gallery around the light and I walked, almost against the splendid windows, around the circumference.

What a place to look out upon that ocean world! Far out the other Orkneys rested upon the sea, hazed with afternoon sun. Near in, under the feet of my lighthouse (no one who stands alone on top of such a gorgeous place could ever think of it as belonging to anyone else but *him*) the waves rolled into the rocks and watered the flowering sea-pink with spray.

Far out the gulls had joyfully spied a skein of fish in the bluest part of the sea and were turning and diving upon it like a winged roundabout. I could see John Dennison in his green jersey standing on the rocks far below and pointing to the milling birds. There was a big catch out there. But today they were shearing sheep.

Two careful, sideways, steps around the narrow gallery and I could see the whole northern haunch of the island. The lighthouse had a curious walled garden, immediately below me now, and on the far side of the wall the men had set up a pen of rough wooden fences. They were now out in the distance, their coloured jerseys bright against the ground hues of the island, rounding up the surprised sheep.

It was wonderful to watch from there. The sun was clear and unchallenged now and the scene was bright. They culled the sheep from their distant grazing and gradually encouraged and pushed them towards the prepared pen below my platform. Their delayed voices, their calls and their laughing, and the barking of the running sheepdog, carried to me on the broad back of the salty wind.

Along that edge of the island the rocks were black and bleak, like a petrified storm, and hanging on to them, a hundred yards from the lighthouse were the rusted platforms and machinery of a wrecked steamship. From my perch I could see the red iron spread along the shore, the sea eating into it with every wave, the birds squatting on wheels and boilers, pipes and pumps. When John had done with the sheep I would ask him about that.

I took another two carefully considered steps along the cat-walk and now saw out along the long smooth spine of the island, dun coloured, freckled with pale flowers, patched with dark shadows, ever a backcloth for the movements of the splendid birds. At the southernmost point was a cottage, a little stone stronghold, where John Dennison had once lived for three weeks of a cold spring while his sheep were lambing, and used at times by peat cutters who voyaged to Auskerry. Between the cottage and the lighthouse, throughout the whole of the island there was only one other standing thing — a solitary tongue of stone upright from the earth, like its brother I had seen in the far south-west, the standing stone on The Gugh in the Scillies.

In this northern place men had once bowed to their Sun-god, pale though he was, with the same misty fear as other tribes in islands far away. And it was in the shadow of the standing stone that they worshipped.

The people on Stronsay tell, with quiet delight, the story of the foggy wartime night when a British fighter pilot, controls shot away, dropped down into what he imagined would be an icy sea. Then he saw the surf-line around Auskerry and gladly brought his coughing plane in to land on the little isle, missing the standing stone by a couple of feet. Throughout the thick night he remained in the cockpit, believing himself to be down on a German-occupied island somewhere across the sea. At daybreak, when the mist had thinned, the lighthouse keepers saw the sitting aircraft and ran across the grass and heather towards it. They wore their proper peaked caps and crew-necked blue jerseys and the pilot, imagining them to be German sailors, climbed from his plane, hands held high and bellowed "Kamerad! Kamerad!"

Another shuffle around the lighthouse gallery and the eastern flank of Auskerry was strung out, the sea alive with sunshine, the rocks thrusting out, the grass cool and sweet. In the sharp inlet almost under my tower *The Fairy Queen* was comfortably slotted, like a toy boat prettily painted.

Then some louder more urgent shouts came from below and I saw six of the Shearers galloping over the turf, across the walls of the lighthouse garden, and towards their fishing boat.

Down the stairway I went, the trap door thudding woodenly as my head ducked. Then at a jogging, light-houseman's run I went around the spirals, out of the garden door, and across towards the sheep pen.

Two of the ewes, frightened in the round-up, had leaped

the rocks and had gone into the sea. They were floating tragically in the green, bundles of heavy wool, a few yards off the sharp shore. Two of the men hung over one ledge and, as I arrived, caught one of the animals, pulled her heavily ashore, and jumped back as with an explosive return to life the ewe bounded off.

But the second sheep was out of reach and rescue, and the water was bitterly cold. Around the lighthouse wall, panting across the grass, came John Dennison and the six men with the dinghy from the fishing boat. Like a stretcher party in some battle hurry they slid down the rocks. Magnus and Roy got into the little boat as soon as it was in the sea and pulled it across to the sad, barely floating hump that was a valuable ewe with lambs to tend.

We all stood and watched the drama; the men on the shore with the boy Keith biting his nails with apprehension and the dog half-wagging its tail in puzzlement. From the sea half a dozen impassive seals sat in the waves and watched with occasional shakes of their huge heads.

The youths got to the sheep and Roy got its head from the water and pulled its tongue from the back of its throat. They towed it in to a cleft of pebbles between the rocks where their father waited. There seemed to be some life, some movement, in it. For five minutes John Dennison sweated over it, first giving it artificial respiration, pressing his big hands against its lungs, and then giving it the kiss-of-life, breathing into the gaping mouth. It was a strange thing to see by that isolated shore, in the sun on a Saturday afternoon; a husky man trying to bring an animal to life. But it was for nothing. It was dead. So they left it, heavy and white, on the stones, and went back to the rest of the flock.

*　　*　　*

Alone I went along the shelving rocks, shiny with the clean washing of the sea, until I came to the tangle of machinery on its hard bed. There are few sadder sights than a decomposing ship; something so sure and noble reduced in years to just a few iron giblets.

"Nineteen-twenty-six," John Dennison had told me. "She was called *The Hastings County*. Bergen to somewhere in America, I think. They say she had a boat on board that was going to be used in the rum-running trade, but I don't know. She came in here in a fog but nobody was lost. That's all that's left now. It gets a bit less every winter."

The rusted platforms, the corroded engines and pipes hung on to the toothy shore. Here there was a tangle of cable, here a solidified pump, here the blind face of what had been a steam gauge; all pieces put together by man and left by him to rot on this remote and empty seascape.

Birds wheeled and walked about along these rocks in clouds and parades. Shearwaters, guillemots, the neat kittiwakes, smallest of the gulls, ringed plovers, insistent oyster-catchers, and the darling of the islands, the little tammy norry, the puffin.

The seals who had witnessed the death of the sheep now came in inquisitive convoy along the waves, keeping pace with my walking. I stopped and sat awhile, staring at them. They halted too, gazing out of the water at me with huge curiosity. One became so involved that he attempted to climb on the shoulders of the larger seal in front, apparently to get a better view of me. The others merely stared, something like old gentlemen looking up from their papers in a cobwebby club.

There was a formation of pancake-shaped stones at this point of the shore, around three sides of a rectangle, rising up about four feet from the turf, with loose stones strewn about to the fringe of the sea. "There's another place like it across the island," John Dennison had told me. "The'yre called the Monks' Houses. I don't know whether monks actually lived there, but I've had letters from the people who look after ancient monuments and the like, telling me I mustn't touch them or pull them down, even if it is my island. I wouldn't pull them down anyway. The sheep find them grand shelter in the winter."

Below the Monks' House is a grave, just a scar on the island's edge. No one knows who lies there. Probably just a drowned seafarer, buried where the ocean threw him to the land, perhaps a world away from his home.

There is another grave near the lighthouse, but this has a story. "It was a man, a farmer I think, from one of the islands," John said. "He and another fella were courting the same girl, see, and the other fella up and murdered the farmer and put him in a sack. Well, he tried to put him in the sack but, according to the tale, the sack was too small, so he cut off his head and put that in separate. Then he threw the sack into the sea, but it was washed up here and they guessed, of course, who'd done it, and he got his deserts. Then they buried the other fella, and his separate head, here by the lighthouse. It's a good story, isn't it?"

Tramping across the long back of Auskerry, across the bouncing grass and moss, I came upon patches of wild yellow irises, three or four areas, widely apart. There were fulmers nesting on the flat, far end of the island, some with eggs, some with young birds beneath their full bodies. It was difficult not to walk into them. They would crouch, unseen, until the last second and then rear up with an angry fuss, spitting out a long angry stream of green phlegm. The young fulmers, sweet and round, remained on the ground very still and untrembling, their beaks thrust forward into the moss and only the rolling upward of a yellow eye as a sign that they knew you were standing like an ogre over them.

Beyond the nesting ground was the little house. It was hunched against the wind, with the sea rising and dropping a few yards away. The peat cutters had sometimes lived there and John Dennison was in residence, as he put it, during the lambing season. It was entirely of stone, roof and all, grey and green, and with bright yellow patches of lichen speckled on it. Two high and sturdy walls running parallel for several yards shielded the front door and, by the look of the wool left hanging, provided a roost for the island sheep.

I pushed open the low, hesitant door and suddenly stood, a boy for a moment, in a house that Crusoe himself might have built. It was the most romantic place I have ever seen; one room dimly lit from the overgrown window. A wooden table, crude chairs, boxes, a great black fireplace, driftwood and a kettle. Cooking pots and an empty Vim tin; fishing lines, landing nets, two iron bedsteads folded in one corner. There was a paraffin lamp hanging, some sea boots, and a box of matches by the hearth.

What a place this must have been, I could see. A fine fire climbing the chimney, throwing its redness all around, and the man sitting on the wooden chair, boots off, reading, with a dog nosing the hearth, and dinner just eaten.

And outside the winter sea, and a gale rattling on the door as though it wanted to come in out of the awful night. You would be secure and warm in there, let the storm do its utmost, and in the morning, when the sky was pale from the night's exertions, you could walk down to the shore and hook some willing fish for breakfast.

Later I asked John Dennison if it had indeed been like that. Islandman that he is, he is far from unromantic, and he nodded his head and agreed, then added: "But I always took a couple of bottles o' the hard stuff too."

They were well on with the shearing by the time I returned to the lighthouse. A hundred and more sheep were by then hopping about the island, puzzled by their sudden loss of poundage, whiter than white, while the rest waited in the pen for their turn at the shears. The men went to the fold and grabbed a sheep, bringing it expertly off its feet like a wrestler throws an opponent. They worked, then, with the stupid woolly face trapped between the man's legs, clipping and running the shears quickly under the thick, tangled coats. The sun was dropping now, but the men sweated, drank beer from bottles, and grabbed another animal. "It's the corners that's the most difficult," grinned Rob Miller.

The wool was rolled and tied and John's middle son, Roy, and I pushed it into big sacks. It was oily, difficult to press down because of its resilience, but we managed to get it all stowed in the end. There was a tractor in a shed behind the lighthouse garden, but they couldn't get the engine going so all the sacks had to be carried down to the geo where *The Fairy Queen* was now moving petulantly in a rising sea. They were stowed below, then everybody ate bread and meat and dainty biscuits, drank a couple of pints of tea per man, and we set off again from the island.

Our crew was reinforced now by a ram being taken back to Stronsay, and a homing pigeon who had abruptly and with some relief, by the look of him, dropped on to the deck. It had been a hard day for the boys, as John called them. He passed a bottle of whisky around, but only some of them accepted it. The sea was running long now, thrusting against the boat, but the wind was to our backs and so it was not so bad.

John, at the wheel, said: "There was a man once tried to keep cattle on an island like we keep the sheep there. He left them all the year, just keeping an eye on them, you understand, through a telescope. When he went over there they all but killed him. They'd gone wild; like you see them in the cowboy films. Nobody could get near them. In the end they had to shoot the lot from a boat."

He was pleased enough with the day, despite the drowned ewe. The lambs had been good, the wool was taken and stowed, the day had been fine, and he was heading home for Stronsay. On the following midnight he would be taking his sons out to the trawling grounds and they would be two days and nights at sea. He was a bit anxious about some wedding photographs he had promised to develop, but the lighthouse was all right for another month. So, provided there wasn't a gale and the lifeboat had to be called out, he could plan a few days ahead and also have time to run his pub.

Alongside the jetty at Stronsay he slid the boat. The dog was the first ashore. Then they hoisted the ram up from the deck, followed by the pigeon. The men went off into the growing evening. John looked at his watch. "Just eight," he said with satisfaction. "I said we'd be back in time for his telly."

Ghosts in the Sun

You see them first after crossing the young waterfall between Ventry and Dunquin in Kerry. Turning Slea Head you are abruptly confronted with the huge Atlantic and the dreaming islands.

Some islands you see from afar. They take shape and substance through sea mist or rise from a hazy horizon. Others you discover of a morning logically lying offshore, just outside your mainland window, tethered like placid animals. But with The Blaskets it is different. Quickly, beautifully, they are there, as you turn that Irish coastal road, shining, cloud-touched, bright green, sitting comfortably on a magical sea. There is nothing but to stand and gaze. You feel the excitement of discovery. There seems every chance that they might quite suddenly turn and go away.

Of all the little islands I have seen and walked upon, The Great Blasket was the one I wanted to experience most. My winter reading of the marvellous books that came out of this solitary and singular place, Tomas O'Crohan's *The Islandman*, Maurice O'Sullivan's *Twenty-years Agrowing*, and the fables and memories of the old woman Peg Sayers. They had all lived in that tight village on The Great Blasket, known its winds and sunshine, sampled its everyday hardship and adventure, heard its rocky laughter and its firelit songs, saw it live and sadly die.

There is no one there now. Only the sheep on the steep meadows, the running rabbits and goats, and the seabirds, curiously few and quiet. The village is inhabited by wind and weeds; the tides come in to smooth the white beach although it has remained unruffled since the last ebb. It is a haunted place.

When I first saw the islands it was a bright ocean day, the sea jovial, the sun touching the sea and the lolling rocks of Slea Head and Dun Mor, the last mainland of Europe, and lighting the green bodies of the islands. They were trailing clouds like white manes that day, ragged and strung out from their highest points. There were no boats in the sea, nor birds in the sky, only the intangible isles and the high white trail of a jet airliner streaking for America.

At Dunquin, where the Blasket people now live, I asked for Maurice Daly. A man at Anascaul, in a bar there, had told me that Maurice Daly's father had once righted a capsized curragh, a giant's feat, in a torn sea, and had sat on a stormy rock all night looking into the waves for the body of his drowned companion. Old Tomas O'Crohan remembers the Dalys living on Innis na bro, the far, little island, and how he would go over there to fish for lobster, catch rabbits, and hold the hand of the Daly daughter.

Maurice was in a house at Dunquin, up the pebble and grit road from the harbour, a house that blinked over a stacked cornfield to the ocean and the islands. A round-eyed boy was on the doorstep and a woman came from the passage and asked me in. In the room were five fishermen and a priest. The fireplace was red-leaded and the kettle hung from a chain, just as it used to do in the days of the island living.

I said: "I would like to go across to The Blasket. Will anyone take me?"

They spoke Gaelic among themselves and the priest joined in. It was apparently a topic for serious discussion. Eventually the woman said in English, as though announcing a major decision: "They say they will take you to the island."

* * *

Dunquin harbour is worked into a fold in the fearsome cliffs, like a hidden fortress, kept away from the wild advances of the sea. There are black caves and yellow flowers on the cliffs, and two big cakes of rock on the seaward side of the jetty. It is never, even on the most tame day, a placid place. The cliffs curl all around and the water slops this way and that, jumping and gurgling, and restless, never still, never calm. They can keep no boats in the water there, so they use only the ancient curraghs, the craft of St. Brendan the Navigator, the patron of the peninsula. These they take from the ocean after each voyage so that the sea cannot get them.

Maurice Daly and three other men, all in black trousers and jerseys, came in a uniform tramp down the steep path from the top of the cliff. You could tell that they always walked like this, jogging with knees up high, almost like a dance, because they had lived on islands with steep rocks and difficult places. Maurice had a wide, quiet face. It was easy to see he was an island man just by looking at his eyes. They have special, placid eyes. He told me he was something over forty years of age, but he couldn't remember. I think he was about sixty. He smiled only with his eyes, his hands were like wood and he had a silver chin. "There's not much English in my mouth," he said. "I never saw the inside of a school."

He conversed in Gaelic with the other men. They did not raise their voices, but their words seemed to carry a good distance. They talked to each other from different parts of the rocks and the cliffs and the paths without shouting at all. The curraghs were kept in a sheltered place at the summit of the stone jetty, upturned like black pea-pods, twenty feet long, just tarred canvas stretched across a wooden frame. The four men, with a practised, easy movement, swung one boat up and over their heads and held it there, walking in unison with their strange steps. The boat covered their heads and arms and shoulders, so that it looked like some awful beetle walking to the sea. From inside the hollowed boat I could hear them still talking.

They righted it, and slid it into the purple water slopping around in the kernel of the cliffs. Maurice called me, in Gaelic, but I knew what he meant, and I stepped uncertainly into the boat and felt it bounce under my weight. I chose to face the stern of the curragh, because this was the way I landed up after stepping into the craft and I felt too insecure to alter things. It was a bit like standing on the back of a restless donkey. I was glad I turned that way in the end, however, because otherwise I would have had to sit for three-quarters of an hour watching the rowers sweat and work their way across the waves, and I thought that might have been uncomfortable.

As it was I got a splendid view of all the peninsula of Dingle, the last tongues of the Old World sticking out into the sea, the bright cottages on the hills, and eventually the fine holy mountain of St. Brendan, sitting above all like a fat king on a fat throne.

All the way across, though, I kept turning to see The Great Blasket taking shape. It was so familiar, like reading through a book and finding all the illustrations tucked secretly at the end so that you knew about each one before you saw it. Here it was, the hill and the village, and *an traigh bhan*, the white beach, that I knew so well from the stories of old Tomas and the young O'Sullivan. Although I was not there yet, I could not resist peeping.

We skirted first the fledgling island, Beginis, where the mainlanders put their young sheep to graze today in the fashion of the islanders of the past times. It has a cloth of thick green grass across its low rocks, and at its centre, the end walls only remaining, the ruins of a little house. It looks like two bookends, left standing when the books have been taken away. The men rowed, slicing the water with skinny oars, no width in the blades, but pulling the boat well through the waves arriving in procession from the open ocean. They talked all the time, a polite conversation by the sound of it, with no raised voices, in Gaelic.

We were closer now. I could see the sheep moving across the face of the upturned meadows, the line of the surf embroidering the vivid beach, and the cottages on different levels, like things on shelves.

I turned in the curragh again, to the left this time, looking across the swelling water, past the little island, to the furthest north of the collection, Inis Tuaisceart. They call it the Resting Giant, and so it looks, with a big peaceful face in profile at one end, a broad chest, and hands folded happily across a mighty belly.

The rowers did not turn towards the easy beach, as I thought they would, but went instead straight for the jaws of the rocks below the village. The shadows of the cliffs fell directly across the sea, making it look thicker, richer, and I could hear the waves gurgling into some place I could not see. The men were sweating and breathing deep by the time we sidled between the rocks. I turned and saw them inching the boat into a little saucer of a gulley where a slipway ran down from the upper rocks and into the deep water. This was the place.

This was the place where the Blasket islanders had launched their rough boats to get their food from the sea, where they set out to hunt puffins on the island of Inis na bro to the west, where they carried their dead for burial and their infants for baptism to the parish on the mainland. From here they sailed to hunt the seals in the sea-sealed caves, to go to market with a single sheep or pig, to salvage some wreckage from the sea to help them in their hard lives.

Maurice Daly and his friends took the curragh from the water and laid it keel-up in the place where such boats had been rested for centuries. There was a rusted winch there and some corroded chain. The stones were shaped with the feet of generations of island people.

Here, on this little landing they waited each time a boat came from Dunquin with the mail, with the letters from America from the sons and daughters who had sailed there to find a life and a living. Here the women waited, more than once, while the drowned bodies of their husbands were brought ashore after a storm had caught them in the fishing grounds. Thirteen died one night. From this steep slipway too they brought in joyfully boatloads of wheat from a God-sent wreck that saved them from starvation at the time of the great famine.

I felt I knew them, these people of the sea. I walked up the path they had trodden from the slipway to the bottom of their primitive settlement, and somehow, from the words of Tomas O'Crohan, the thoughts of Maurice O'Sullivan, and the sweet tales of old Peg Sayers, I knew every step of the journey. Had they been there to hold out their hands to me as I came ashore to take me and show me the wondrous Great Blasket, I could not have felt more familiar with the place.

At the head of the rise from the landing place you come

upon the saddest sight. A whole village, a whole life, a whole story, standing in doleful ruin. The houses back up the hill, roofless, windowless, doorless, like a congregation of senile people without teeth or eyes. The paths that joined the village doors are running with weeds, harsh grasses, and, poetically, forget-me-nots. Strangely it is the round house with the turf roof just above the landing, the place where they sheltered sheep, that has kept whole. The human habitations have, for the most part, decayed and died.

But not all. Maurice Daly led me up the wriggling path to the southern end of the village and to a house that was bigger, sturdier than the rest, a house with a roof and with shutters at the windows. The other men who had rowed the curragh were there before us. A door of the house was open and they were inside.

They sat, three of them, on wooden chairs and watched expectantly as a wood-fire they had just lit grew in the black grate. There was a bulky kettle suspended from a chain, just like the one I had seen on the mainland. The kettle was old and scaled, burned with different scars, and the flames of the new fire were working away below it.

"Sean O'Sullivan, this man here in this chair. This was his house." Maurice spoke carefully, working out the English beforehand. The other men nodded. None of them spoke any tongue but Gaelic. "It was his house," repeated Maurice as a man repeats a foreign sentence when he is reasonably sure he has it right. "When he lived on The Blasket."

Whenever Sean made the crossing now he went to his old house and sat in the kitchen as he had done in the days far gone. He boiled a kettle and made tea at the hearth with the kettle his mother had used.

It was a remarkable room. It had been left for many years and the dust and damp had got to it. But there was a great dresser lined with cups, saucers, plates and pots, and embroidered with cobwebs. There were some books, soggy with mildew, on a shelf, the wooden pieces of furniture, and hanging in the rafters were fishing nets and floats, unused for long and housing cities and nations of spiders and other insects.

The kettle boiled and they made some tea. Sean took a cup from the dresser, poured some for me and handed it over. He made very good tea. Maurice said: "The place died, you see. All the young went over the water and that was the end of it."

I said it was a shame. "I'm not one that's sorry," he said. "It was hard here."

I went from the house and towards the village again. "That house," Maurice called after me. "Down there. Maurice O'Sullivan who wrote the book, that was his. He was my kin."

"Which is Tomas O'Crohan's house?" I called back.

"Over there," he pointed. "The house with no roof."

None of them had roofs. But I could see where he pointed and I went that way. The whole aspect of the island village and beyond was in view now. The ruins and that incongruous circular hut for sheep, the paths and the pastures, and beyond the lovely white wideness of the beach. The sun was full, flowing all over the island, and it was not difficult to imagine how fine and free life must have been on a day in summer like this, with the sea friendly, the other islands green and fair, and the mainland reassuringly distinct.

It was the fogs and rain, the storms and the danger that were so different. The reefs that had finally torn and sunk the pathetic survivors of the Armada had taken the island seafarers too. On many a winter's night the curraghs risked everything to fetch a mainland priest to an old islander who needed to see one before dying.

No, this sort of summer's day would have been one of the good days. A day for swimming or pulling in fish, or lying on the high ground with a girl and making love and poems. The islanders were very good at both and the poems remain, although love has gone a long time and the highland heather is empty of young people.

Looking back from that place on that crystal day, over the big shoulder of the island, beyond the place where Maurice Daly still stood, I could see Little Skellig and Skellig Michael humped in the sea. The two, distant, rocky islands, triangular against the sky, were trailing pennants of clouds like tents at a medieval tourney.

Turning again I took the tilting path that went across the top of the village, until I came to the ruin that was once Tomas O'Crohan's little house. Like the others it is just bones now, with daisies and forget-me-nots studding the grass that cushions it. From the bank behind the house on that day I could look across the strait to Dunquin and see the tip of the church where old Tomas now lies dead, across the sea, but not too far from his cottage.

I hesitated to go through the door. How many times in his wondrous life had this islandman gone under that thick stone lintel. Across to the old woman over the yard taking a rabbit for the pot, and getting a story in return; or to cut peat only to come home dissatisfied because the island poet had kept him all day listening to words; or to launch the curragh to take fish, or sometimes men, from the sea.

I went in. There was just the shape of one room, the pointed stone ends, the low side walls, the holes where the windows once shone, and the roof showing the sky. It was like a man without a head. Tomas lived here then. Tomas the wise, the gentle, the poetic. Plaques have been placed on the walls of lesser men, but here there were only dandelions.

It was easy to see how they built the houses, crouched under the high bank, huddled down out of the weather, with the turf and the flowers growing over the roofs. The hens of the village used to nest in the roof and Tomas himself relates how his father once had a new-laid egg drop into his plate as he sat at supper. Then a village simpleton fell through a neighbour's roof while searching, he explained, for his mother's lost pig.

The walls retained a trace of whitewash and there were some flakes of green paint sticking around the door. The fireplace was smeared an indelible black and the hook where they fixed the kettle was in the wall. Beside the fireplace was the small hole where the family used to keep their treasured clock.

In here, and in the narrow room behind the hearth, they all lived. Parents and running children, tots under the tables, dogs, cats, geese, chickens, and probably a pig or a cow too. The fire used to eat through the peat, and the lamps of seal-oil made crescents of light on the mysterious walls. All the howling of sea and wind could not touch them here. They would crouch and stumble along the village paths, going from house to house, finding a place for warmth and stories, and they were never disappointed. There was always somewhere.

These people never tasted tea or sugar before the turn of the century. When a boy was brought a pair of boots or a new jacket from the mainland it was the custom that he visited every house in the village to display his finery. He would knock at the doors and they would admire him and give him a potato and perhaps a kiss and send him on.

Only one thing has remained with the place in the years since the last islanders pushed their curraghs away from the shore and went to seek somewhere new. The essence of it, its *being*, is still there. You realise it as you stumble through mossy yards and by dead walls. You can almost smell the damp serge, and the peat-smoke. Their shades seem to brush by you on your solitary walk, hurrying about their daily work. You can hear them singing and telling hushed stories.

Here, on this sunlit day with the sky big and open and the sea so happy, it was like being in a ghostly old house.

The path that cuts through the village runs at roof level past Tomas's house. The grass was firm and soft so I sat and opened the lunch basket the hotel had given me. Automatically, and then abruptly with an odd guilt, I began to unpack the plastic plates, the nice cup and saucer, the cutlery, the cold meats and salad, and the thermos that the hotel had provided. There was a neat white cloth meant for the grass and dainty cartridges of salt and pepper. The guilt seized me about half-way through the dismantling of the picnic. I found myself looking up and about to make sure I was alone. I was. I could see the movements of Maurice Daly and the other men on the green skyline, a long way off.

I shrugged, spread the little cloth, arranged the salad on the plastic plate, and doggedly bit into a leg of chicken. Then I looked up, across the skeleton of the village, and then down again through the open roof of Tomas's house into the ruined room. The meat died in my jaws. I stopped chewing. Comically, I suppose, I scrambled all the bits of the untouched picnic together and jammed them back into their container. Then I got up and walked away from the place. It seemed the only decent thing to do.

Taking the higher path I came first to the village well, a tongue of water falling into a pool, clear but looking bored with disuse. I had heard that the lack of water was one of the reasons for evacuating the island, but I never believed it. No Irishman ever left anywhere for lack of water.

Up here too was the King's House. They always had a King on Blasket, one man who through wisdom and personality led all the rest and made the decisions. His house was bigger, and the elder men would sit there and talk about their life and how it should be ordered. They laid the law and the punishments, they decided on crops and fishing,

6—SLI

arranged marriages, and defences against probing revenue officers from the mainland.

The King had the final word, always, and he was never disputed. Once, when they had been hunting puffins for winter eating on one of the out-islands, they returned and rowed ashore into the hands of a bailiff and other forbidding officers. The puffins, it appeared, were private puffins belonging to a lady landowner on the mainland.

The Blasket islanders went to court, simple, primitive men, used only to the outdoors and the traps of nature, suddenly confronted with the great indoors and a crafty prosecution lawyer. But they had a lawyer too and they stood dumbly and listened as he spoke in their defence. According to the story, which, this being Ireland, could be just a story or an apocryphal tale, the prosecution man was a clever bird from Dublin, who scorned the little man from Dingle championing the Blasket men. At one point, his voice booming in the cold courtroom he asked: "And has not my learned friend on the other side ever heard of the well-known principle of law, *misera est servitus ubi jus est aut incognitum aut vagum*?" The islandmen stood petrified at the sound of the words. But their man was good. "On The Great Blasket," he replied quietly, "the talk is of little else." The islanders won their case.

From the King's House the island track went like a rim around the northern hump of the island, above the fields where the exiled islanders at Dunquin still keep their sheep and goats; tidy fields enclosed with tidy stone walls, and with deep lanes cosseting flowers. Set into one of the lane walls, as a strengthener at a cornice, was a rusted piece of tackle from some ship of long ago.

The day was brilliant and hot now. I reached the sheer cliffs opposite Inis Tuaisceart, the peaceful island like a giant stretched out on the ocean, a floating man, on his back and sleeping. From there you could hear his snores in the deep breathing of the sea. The sun was warm on the grass of the cliff and bright on the water. Below me the waves were torn apart on the rocks and came back, as they always do, for more. The furious white that frothed over the humps and ridges below died into long bandages unravelling out into the heavy blue further away.

I sat and looked one way to Tiaracht, a warrior of a rock resting in the placid Atlantic far out. Powerful, triangular, you could imagine how it merely shrugs its shoulders at the worst of winter's storms. It has a lighthouse and, in the old years, when people from The Blaskets left for America, they could see the shining light as their ship went away. It was the last memory they carried with them of their homes and all they were leaving.

The cliffs of The Blasket fell down from where I sat in the sun, now without conscience, drinking the tea from the flask. They fell all around as far as I could see to the east, like a many-pleated skirt worked with a fine embroidery of flowers and ferns and the different hues of their rocks.

Above the camel-back of the hill behind me a solitary chimney peeped like a fugitive looking from a hiding-place. Up there, at the centre of the island, is a tower which some-one built as defence against Napoleon. A French ship once fired a single cannon-ball at it, and missed. Later, more efficiently, it was demolished by lightning.

When I turned towards the mainland again, now som-nolent and indistinct in the summer haze, I could look down directly on the full stretch of the magnificent undisturbed beach, the white strand of the islanders. The small flat islands were fiery green in the channel beyond. A few big white birds pushed up the straits, but there was nothing else moving, no jets high up, no boats below; only the birds and the sea.

Down the fields I walked then, through the lanes shel-tered and deep as infantry trenches, over the great loaves of stone that formed the walls, and finally down a gulley to the beach.

The gulley must have been begun by water seeping from the peat bog at the top of the island, but it had taken its shape by the walking, running and rushing of years of people. Here the wrecks came ashore, or the revenue officers, breathless whales or drowned men. This was the point of fortune and of sorrow. The steep gulley down which I slithered had heard many feet, shouts and laughter and tears.

What a beach that was! A huge flat palette of the purest sand, marked only by driftwood which had arrived on the morning tide, enjoyed, that day anyway, only by a small touring party of sandpipers and a couple of strangely reticent oyster-catchers. It was not the sort of place where you might make a success of a deck-chair concession.

Waves ran in from the open channel and fell, like lace across the level sand. It was very solitary being there in that wide empty place. I sat uncomfortably for a while, looking at the reassuring hills of Kerry, and then got up. I went across the width of the beach, from arm to arm, dragging my feet deep into the sand, leaving a ploughed trail behind me. When I got to the far side it looked very odd furrowed out of the flat sand. It did not make me feel much better, but at least it gave the beach a look of having been lived in.

I climbed the gulley again and walked all the tunnelled lanes until once more I was at the village. The fine day was fading, going quietly away beyond the humped back of The Great Blasket. The little ruined houses sank deeper into their own shadows. I went through the door of Tomas's house for a final look. Then in and out of the yards, past the round sheep-house, and to a place at the cliff edge, all nettles now, and among them pieces of stone stuck upright in the earth. This was the place where, in the old times, they buried unbaptised infants and suicides who could not lie in consecrated ground.

Maurice Daly and the others were at the landing-place getting the curragh in the water. It was cool and shadowed down there. We pushed out into the evening channel, the last light on the drowsy sea. We went back a different way because the current had swung about with the tide. The men rowed and talked in their even Gaelic. All the way back I was facing the island, looking at the beach and the houses until they were too distant and it was too dim to see them at all.

I thought then of the words that Tomas wrote — that he wanted to "set down the character of the people about me so that some record of us may live after us, for the like of us will never be again...."

The Ocean Mountain

It was one of those fragile mornings you get in the West.
The Irish say they're 'soft mornings'; a little obligatory
rain at first, just to keep the dust down, and then the
sun filtering through the clouds and running into the streets,
and making a warm day of it. It was a good day for going
to Skellig.

Jeremiah O'Connor was sitting on a stone on the quay at
Cahirciveen, Valentia Island green over his left shoulder.
The night before I had telephoned him from Tralee to ask
him to take me to the great rock, Skellig Michael. " 'Tis
not a place you can run a bus service to, you'll understand,"
he had said. "Now get on the 'phone to me in the morning
and I'll tell you what the sea says."

He was a short man, pensive and slow-moving. His cap
looked as though it had been screwed tight on his head. He
wore a woolly pullover which had drifted a bit in several
directions and hung around his middle like a fishing net. He
was somewhere in his sixties and he told me he had been

sailing out to Skellig, when the sea allowed him, for forty years, and he had never climbed the rock.

"Don't suppose I shall now," he said philosophically. "There's six hundred steps and I'm not much good on the stairs these days."

He was very sure on the boat, though. It was nudging the jetty impatiently, a brawny boat, smelling of oil and fish, with the engine in a box amidships, and a high-built prow. A working boat, honest, like a good carthorse. She was about thirty feet long and there was a nine-year-old called Peter, a handsome Anglo-Indian lad, at the tiller.

"Brought this boat up from Baltimore Yard in 1930," said Jeremiah, climbing down and giving the engine a little oil like a nurse doling medicine. "She was lovely then, and she's still good now. Stronger and better than some of the stuff they go to sea in these days. It's sixteen miles out to Skellig. Take about two hours."

The first half was voyaging through the close herd of islands that stand about Valentia and shelter the demure inner passage at Cahirciveen from the strength of the big ocean. The boat coughed along amiably, sending out short smoke signals from its pipe. At the tiller the young boy, his brown face alive with the joy of navigating, watched the shoals and passages, and eased the boat confidently through them. "Fine lad," said Jeremiah lighting his pipe. "His father's come from India with him. Loves the sea and the boats."

Valentia, a fat bean of an island, sheltered our passage to the open sea. It has a rising green back, reticent cottages spaced over its fields, and a brainy brow of headland facing the Atlantic. It was here that Marconi brought ashore his first ocean telegraph cable, tugging it from the seabed with the other end triumphantly fast in America.

Jeremiah was, for some reason I forget, telling me about the connor fish. "Now that's a strange fish," he mused. He had a marvellous face when he talked, solemn and yet moving with life. "A very strange fish, I'd say. I remember catching a connor when I was a lad there in Cahirciveen and I thought 'I'll cook this one for me tea,' and so I did. Never did I taste a thirstier fish than that one, mister. I ran down to the bar and I estimate it was six pints before that fish was satisfied. Aye, it cost me a lot that connor fish."

He sniffed at the air as though trying to get a taste of the swell from the open ocean which was booming beyond the guardian wall of islands and headlands before the bow. The estuary about us remained as undisturbed as a country river. On the neck of land to starboard a painted village moved by. "Portmagee," said Jeremiah. "There's a good woman lives over there now who was thirteen years on Skellig lighthouse. She used to look after the men and their families out there.

"Thirteen years and she never saw a blade o' grass nor a sheep nor heard a whistlin' bird. Only that great big wet rock. There's a thing, mister."

The booming of the muscular oceanic waves on the other side of the barrier islands came loud now, like someone banging a door with a big fist. Inside the estuary the water jumped about fretfully. Terns flew down from the cliffs, swinging and crying above us. "Thirteen years on Skellig," mused Jeremiah returning to his theme. " 'Tis a terrible long time. The light men used to stay out there for five years at one time. It did some strange things to them. But even Skellig doesn't touch The Tiaracht over beyond The Blaskets. I saw a man from that lighthouse come to a bar in Cahirciveen once. He'd been out there for 126 days without seeing anyone but the other keeper. He was like a ghost. Very thirsty too."

Now we could see the Atlantic. The islets were riven with holes and hollows, and as we chugged by, still in good water, we could see the ocean through the gaps, like looking through keyholes. The ageing boat gave a long wheeze from its engine, almost a resigned sigh.

She took it bravely enough, wheeling about, around the last hem of islets and rocks, away from the last shelter, and rode out on to the great purple swell running spectacularly towards us and Ireland. The front of the boat heaved to meet the bright sky, the boy at the tiller called in delight, and I wrapped myself tighter around my stomach.

For a moment the boat quivered at its highest, like a pawing horse, then fell down frontwards into a trough, the stern rearing high and the boy in the stern still hooting wildly. It was no storm, not even the shirt-tail of a storm; it was a splendid day, dazzling bright, with a great static heaven and good sun. But it was an Atlantic swell, a great progressive rolling of the sea beneath a still sky; the famous double-act, the sea and the sky, one doing the acrobatics, the other impassive, facing the audience, arms folded.

"Puffin Island out there," said Jeremiah as though he were sitting in a deep armchair. He got up and put some oil from a can into the coughing engine. He was old but steady, like a pensioner putting coal on the fire. "Took a woman out there once, from America. Didn't see a puffin all the long day. She wanted her money back."

But now I could see the Skelligs. When the bow dipped and the waves were not too high I could see across their shoulders to the horizon and the twin islands. Little Skellig was the nearer, where the gannets lived, where no man would land unless it was a dead flat day and he was wild about gannets.

Then big Skellig Michael just beyond, an outsize hat of a rock, an ocean stronghold, six hundred feet of mountain sticking from the waves. A rock, an island, a lovely fabled place.

There was still a lot of bumping sea to go, but at least I could see them. Every few dips of the bow they came on my horizon again. Closer, just a little, each time.

I felt good on the boat with old Jeremiah and the boy. Every time I breathed I took great lungfuls of salt. The colours of the water, the outlines of the briny islands, and the clear sun, exhilarated me. Jeremiah was quietly sitting, I thought perhaps wondering if the engine needed some more oil, and the lad Peter was happily hanging over the tiller like a farmboy over a gate.

Then a marvellous thing happened. It was something like those heroic film sequences, all vivid colours and immense waves, spray on the faces, and suddenly a shout: "Shark on the port bow!"

It was Peter who shouted, all but falling over the big arm of the tiller in his bursting excitement. He actually howled: "Look! Look, Jeremiah. A big fish."

There it was, a hundred yards off, frothing and fighting the waves, a monstrous shark, silver, muscular; jumping out of sea into sun. My memory of those seconds tells me it was a hundred feet long. Caution tells me it was nearer twenty-five. But I prefer to think of it as a hundred. "That's a bloody fine fish," said Jeremiah from under the peak of his cap. He stood up, sat down again, and had another look at the engine.

I found myself on my feet, clutching the boat and yelling juvenile yells in the direction of the leaping shark. The thrill of seeing the free, flashing fish, and shouting into the wind from that bucking boat will be with me when I rummage around for dreams to dream in my old age.

The boy and I called at it to jump again. And it did. For us. It accomplished a prodigious, curling, spinning movement, clear of the water, and crashed down in spray again. "Again! Again!" called Peter, fighting with the tiller. "Do it again, shark!" The shark obeyed, heaving in the hefty sea. I let go of the boat at the wrong time, just as a swollen roller took it under the keel and lifted it towards the sky. Off-balance I came very near to joining the shark, but Jeremiah leaned casually forward and caught me by the arm, pulling me back into the boat. "Yes," he said meditatively. "A bloody fine fish."

We didn't see the shark again. Nor were there any boats or ships. We were alone on the Atlantic, or our bit anyway, with the islands growing over the bow.

"There was a day," said Jeremiah, "when this place you see was full o' fishing boats after mackerel. From everywhere they came down here to work the sea. I was a lad and I got seven shillings for a week's fishing, and the harbour at Cahirciveen was all boats. Boats from all over Ireland and England and the Isle of Man, and distant parts like that. And the Frenchmen, they came up too. And the town was full of them, and there was drinking and singing in the bars until late every night."

He paused and I thought he was going to make for the engine with the oil can again, but he didn't. He said: "A hundred boats a time landing their catches. That's a lot of mackerel and trains running through the night to get the catch to the markets. It was a grand place Cahirciveen in those times, mister. Yesterday I went to the wake of O'Neil, and he was the last of the old fish buyers. His father was a fish buyer too. O'Neil was the last one, and it was a fine wake he had too. They give you a good send-off in these parts."

Now we were not far off Little Skellig. What a wild, screaming place. Twin rocky peaks made white, like an iceberg by all the tribes of sitting gannets. From a mile the rocky island seemed solid with them, with the black rock only a skirting where it dropped into the fast sea. Skellig Michael, like an ocean castle, was a further two miles away, green and blue in the August sea, with few birds upon it.

There was a commotion beneath the bow, and again Peter called out and pointed. A brown fledged bird, fat and frightened, was trying to get out of our way. It flopped across the water like a stage funnyman falling over his own boots. It flapped a few feet then fell on its face, squawking ridiculously, pulled itself out of the water and repeated the act. It was a young gannet, a stupid ungainly brown bird, overloaded with puppy-fat, or the ornithological equivalent, and foolish with fear. It was a rag-bag creature, and yet it would one day become a grave, graceful white bird like one of those who now curved about the boat in a wide loop, dancers in the sky. Its shaggy brown covering, like a mothy fur coat, becomes all white, tapered feathers; the body slims, and an expression of elegant self-possession replaces the startled look of the flapper.

The strait between the two Skelligs was running rough. A fishing boat appeared to the east and we could see in its huge dip and lift a reflection of our own movements across this curling sea.

Little Skellig went by. All the cassocked birds were ranged like choirs along the flutes and pipes of rock. There were millions, I was convinced, simply sitting and occasionally moving up one place, perhaps like people queue to get into heaven. Some eased out their wings and joined the flying formations about the peaks of rock and around our little boat, calling mysteriously and then going back once more into one of the long lines. On a gannetry life seems simple but busy. There is always something to do.

There is a hole in the lower spine of Little Skellig, at the water level. The rock arches out over the hole like a tail or a tiller. Once your boat has run by this you are within sight of the landing side of Skellig Michael.

That flank of the rock rises sheer from the island's foot to its forehead. The landing place, like all landing places on exposed islands, is tucked craftily into an elbow of rock, the fatherly arm keeping out the worst of the waves.

"There's days," said Jeremiah uncoiling a rope on the deck boards, "when we struggle out here and then it's too dangerous to get in. If the sea is running with the wrong wind you could never do it."

"It's all right today, isn't it?" I asked anxiously. I didn't want to have to turn away now we had come this far.

"Today is just about right," he said. The boat had sniffed around the bend in the rock and, almost enclosed now from the sea, come to heel alongside a concrete jetty. I stepped across the boards, on to the side, and up to the firm step of the landing place. I was ashore on big Skellig Michael.

Looking up was like looking from the base of a big hole. A funnel of dripping rock went up hundreds of feet until it broke out into the blue sky. It was not as forbidding as it might have been because all the way down to the foundation stones around me it was planted and hung with a plump mossy plant of vivid and friendly green.

"The steps are over there, mister," called Jeremiah from the boat. "We're off fishing. We'll pick you up in three hours. I'm hoping you don't mind climbing stairs."

I had no choice anyway. The steps cut into the rock went up from the landing place, skirting the very edge of this island mountain. I waited until Jeremiah and the boy had put the boat out into the sea again and were turning its nose to some place south where they knew there were mackerel. Then I looked out towards Little Skellig again, looking all the more now like something that had floated down from the Arctic Ocean.

All that day, turning odd corners of the rocky staircase, climbing over boulders, I was to see it again and again, its bird-white accentuated by the intense blue of the summer sea. To the few men on Skellig Michael now, and to those who lived lonely lives there in the past, Little Skellig must be, and has been, as familiar and comforting as the house next door.

At a steady climb I took the path. There was always a wall of wet rock on my right and a spectacular drop into the nagging sea on the other side. Water streamed from every crease and pore in the strata, feeding small settlements of pale flowers lodged in the cracks and keeping that strange hedgehog-shaped moss moist and bright green like the grass of the most well-nourished meadow.

Rocks and light contrive strange shapes and tricks, especially when, as in this place, they are set against the single sky. Half-way up the climb to the lighthouse on a jutting shelf of slabs and moss was a rock, so worked by the centuries of wind, so caught by the sun and shadow of that moment, that it looked like a jagged piece of modern metallic sculpture. It leans forward nervously over the huge drop to the sea, thin and so full of sorrow, like a starved angel.

"We call that the Wailing Woman." The voice came quietly but suddenly enough to startle me.

He was a slight man with a mariner's face and a smattering of beard. He was Jim Power, a good name for a lighthouse keeper, which he was. "Everybody that ever sets a foot here stands looking at her," he nodded. "Funny what shapes things take when the gales and the salt have time to work on them. Now that wouldn't look out of place in a fine gallery of art, now would it?"

He had two other keepers with him on Skellig, Reg Sugrue and Jim Tweedy. Each man spends a month with the light and then goes ashore for two weeks. Reg Sugrue met us half-way up the dripping path, standing by the ribbed crane which they use to haul supplies from the servicing vessel which the Commissioners of Irish Lights send regularly. It does not come in at the little lower landing but slots itself into a natural pen in the rising rock, away from the bite of the biggest waves.

Reg Sugrue was a broad, easy man. You could imagine him shouting on the nastiest of nights and still making himself heard over the wind. "See the cape over there," he said as the three of us walked towards the lighthouse. "Well, that's where I live, County Cork. And Jim here lives right next door to me. You'd think we had enough of being neighbours out here, wouldn't you, but our wives keep each other company.

"On a calm night when it's clear you can see the lights of our town and I've stood out here and watched them go out one by one. And they can see the lighthouse beam too."

We had walked to a generous horseshoe in the cliff-way covered with a sloping roof of red corrugated iron, curiously like the sort of tented way they put up for kings and queens. "That's to stop rocks rolling on your head," said Reg, nodding up as we went under the arch. "They're always slipping and dropping. You get a very strange feeling some nights that there's someone sitting up on top rolling the things down at you."

At the top of the track was the lighthouse, although you climb to it at such an angle, eventually clambering into a small door into a courtyard, that you cannot see the tower of the light.

Some new fuel tanks had been built within the enclosed yard, taking up most of the only bit of level area on Skellig. The new cement was covered with sacking, and the sacks were covered with Chinese writing and the one name Hong Kong in English. Strange how far even an everyday bag can wander.

Jim Power took me up to the light; a short run of steps and we were standing right beside it, the same huge and delicate robot which I had seen swinging on that lonely flat island of Auskerry in the Orkneys. Then with all the serious pride of a housewife with a new cooker, the keeper said: "We've got the electricity now, you see. The light's been shining here since 1826, but we only went over to the electric this year. The fuel tanks outside, that's for running it. It means we've got central heating in the lighthouse as well, and that's a blessing, no mistake."

Looking out from the top of the tower through the light's own window was like looking through the vizor of some giant warrior in armour. From up there firm and sure on the island rock, the ocean seemed to flatten out and became respectably mild. The edges of the world were blurred with mist, and the sea was very local and pondish. Then I saw Jeremiah's boat making for the mackerel, miles down it seemed from my perch, and I realised it was still heaving against a muscular sea.

On a higher perch of the rock-island they used to have a position from which they fired maroons on foggy nights. But it was a hard, dangerous climb for the man who had to do the firing. So they fixed an electrical device to fire each maroon, with the operator sitting comfortably within the lighthouse.

A single maroon exploding is a loud enough bang, but on Skellig one thick night a fault in the electrical circuit detonated three hundred *all at once*. The lighthouse men swore that the great island actually jumped from the sea. Everyone was stone deaf for days. After that, on foggy nights, one man made the climb to the maroon platform just to ensure that the things went off one at a time.

Down below I went again. Reg had made some tea in the mess room where there was a new electric stove, a television set, and a picture of the Virgin Mary all on one wall. I signed the visitors' book and saw that the last signature was that of Mrs. Barbara Castle, Minister of Transport for Great Britain, doubtless getting away from the traffic.

Now I wanted to climb higher up the towering spiked rock to the shelf, almost at the summit, where centuries ago a settlement of gale-blown monks had lived and prayed. It was not a journey for anyone susceptible to vertigo. I climbed, infinitely careful with each foot-place, the curling stairway cut into the rock. It went up the terrifying chimney

7—SLI

of Skellig, disappearing at the top into the sky, it seemed, like a wisp of smoke.

I had to grope some of the way. The steps were slippery and fractured, the bright green moss, wet as sponge, piled about them. I went close by the Wailing Woman, marvelled again at the thinness of the carved rock and heard her moans as the wind went about her. Up there too was a stone hut, incongruously like a bus-shelter, appended to the last few feet of a jutting ledge, with a great whistling drop directly into the mouth of the ocean far below.

The wind was skidding about me up there, sliding around the taller rocks, bouncing from the smaller boulders. But the sun was clear and encouraging too, warm on my head as I climbed, compensating for the edge of the wind. I had to rest now and again, balancing, circus fashion it seemed, on a flat stair of stone, perched half-way to the sky. It was while I was hesitating thus, needing to recover my breath and then recover my balance, that I heard a cock crow.

Out there, on that salty precipice, I could hardly have been more astonished if one of Mrs. Castle's traffic wardens had appeared with fussy notebook and belligerent ball-point. A cock crowing! A cosy farmyard sound, the sort of thing you heard in a warm hayloft, or across the early fields. But not out in the ocean.

It gave a confirmatory crow. I crept up a few more steps and looked over a sort of chute in the strata, a hard channel that ran down to the lighthouse men's path. Below, pecking at some scattered corn, was a clutch of hens, with a dazzling cockerel proud on a rock, preparing for another shout and watching some circling gulls, who, in turn, were watching the corn.

I went on. This part, this dizzy gulch, they call Christ's Saddle. Now each knee had to be raised high and each foot carefully placed. Two-thirds of the ascent were behind me when I realised that the crooked stairway suddenly had the sea on both sides instead of just one. The new drop was on the left, a wondrous petrified place of rocky profiles, hollowed by the winds of the world. It staggered down in great sections until it reached the inky sea.

This was a summer's day, with gulls and gannets flying cheerfully, but that narrow place seemed the most exposed and loneliest bridge in the world. How those ancient monks must have crawled up that terrible face, chipping out that staircase of rock, clinging and crouching as they worked while the rain fell and the hard wind beat upon them.

The final ascent to the platform where the monks had lived was steeper, more twisted, and very thrilling. It was like walking along a plank in the sky, with the wind and the sun for company, and the sea, almost desultory in its movements from that height. I did a cautious half-turn and stood against the wind, looking down over the stony skirts of this strange island. One of the lighthouse men was moving along far below on the path, driving a little electric truck, carrying boxes from the landing place to the storehouse on the chin of Skellig.

I could see Jeremiah and Peter at their distant fishing. At least I could see the boat, nuzzling at the waves that looked to me no more than folds and little creases. Then I looked straight over the wide leg of sea to the mainland. Cork and Kerry lay idly over there, sleepy and remote. There was the massive Bull Rock; there gentle Dursey Island.

A few more steps through a crawling entrance they call the Needle's Eye and I was on the mossy plateau, the high place. They dedicated Skellig Michael to the Patron Saint of High Places; and this was the most westerly of all the fortresses of Christendom in the old world.

A lofty, lonely, peaceful citadel. Fourteen hundred years ago those strange, hard men, the monks, built themselves bee-hive huts up here on this windy roof. They made them of flat stones, laid tightly together, and without mortar or mud or anything else to bind them. They are still there, these little domes, lived in now by the stormy petrels and sometimes other birds. Six huts, two oratories, and the surviving bones of a little church.

Anyone who has climbed to that solitary situation, I imagine, does one thing when they arrive. They sit down. I sat on the thick cushioned moss, breathless from the climb, and took in the details. The sensation was, at the same instant, both humbling and thrilling.

There were some ancient crosses, worn thin as razor blades, projecting crookedly from the moss. Here the monks lie in shallow earth brought in handfuls to the soil-less cemetery. The figured window of the church still occupies the middle of a single wall, standing but hunched. Without moving I could see the white cake, Little Skellig, two miles over the ocean, and over the broken back of the wall the thoughtful coast of County Kerry.

I went to the first bee-hive hut. The door was almost hugging the ground, but I crouched and crawled in. From a heady, clear, high mountain, I was, in two steps, taken into the gut of the world, or so it seemed. The darkness within was thick, pressing down on the back of my head; I could feel it and I could smell it. I could not stay there. Like an animal out of a burrow I backed away. Ah, there I was! At the top of the earth and the sea, the sharp air blowing into my face, above me the bursting sky and the free flying birds. I didn't go in again.

I walked into what had been the chancel of the little chapel, facing the window on the sea, and found in the moss the place where, recorded by a half-capsized stone, Patrick and William Callaghan, the two small sons of a lighthouse man, lie buried. They died in the middle of the last century. One was two, one four years old. What an odd, encompassed world they knew for that little time.

But this was a lively day. I walked to the higher moss, saw the bright well that had, almost miraculously, given the monks their water, and then I stretched out and contemplated the sky for a long time. The sun was strong and uninterrupted, and behind the monk's beautifully built wall I was away from the feelers of the wind.

Later I would have to stutter down to the landing place again, go over the blowy sea in the small boat, and end up with Jeremiah and a Guinness in the pub at Cahirciveen.

But all that could wait for a while. A stormy petrel and a fulmer made tracks across the sky, other birds came and went. I could hear the vying whispers of the wind and waves.

There was I on the afternoon of August Bank Holiday Monday, far from the cars and the crowds, lying on a bed of moss, atop a mountain in the Atlantic Ocean. There was no resisting the temptation. "Hello! Hello!" I shouted, half laughing at the stupidity of it. "Hello! Anyone there?" I yelled straight up at heaven. I would not have been surprised if I'd got an answer.

But I didn't. I was completely alone.

7 CLEAR ISLE

"Can I get there by Candle-light?"

Now that was a fine night at O'Regan's. The finest for a long time, they said, with some good varied voices and some steady drinking. The older island men, in their square caps and their shiny black suits, sat quietly about the lamp-lit wall singing shyly, with hardly a sound. The young people from the mainland, from Skibbereen and Baltimore, and the most vocal from the County Tipperary, sang loudly and well, sitting on the floor among the mugs and the glasses.

Every one of the Clear Isle men, it seemed, had the same face and the same voice. Each face was long, tough and narrow, like the boats they used, with their eyes sharp and blue. When they took their caps off, which was only at Mass or when it got too hot in O'Regan's, they had a white band of skin at the top of their foreheads, because the sun and the wind never got to them there.

A boy had a flute, a young girl a piping penny whistle, and someone else a guitar. Everybody had voices and glasses. They were mostly rebel songs, naturally, about the Wearing of the Green, and the Boys from Tipperary, which, hearing them now, half a century after the blood and the battles, made me thankful that the Irish can sing as well as fight. Everybody had to sing a solo, or recite, or do something. A young German, who had somehow strayed to that old island, organised a vague sort of game where everybody had to throw coins into a Guinness glass full of water. There were shocked faces all around. No one had ever seen a Guinness glass full of water before.

A young man sprang up and shouted: "Attention of the house, if you please, for Mr. Gilhouley, who will give us 'The Boston Burglar'." Then thrashing out his hand: "Mr. Gilhouley!"

"Sit down, Dermot," said Mr. Gilhouley patiently and quietly from the floor. "I'm not singin' as yet. I'm clearing me t'roat with this drink, can't you see."

All the voices started up, but Dermot thrust them to silence again, flinging his arms wide and shouting the first lines of a poem:

> When I was a lad in the Kerry Hills
> And the tinkers came to town...

It went on a bit, but it was a stirring poem, and everyone drank quietly while he went through it. He sat down with applause and a red face and then leaped to his feet again, waving his hand extravagantly: "Ladies and gentlemen," he announced, "Mr. Gilhouley and 'The Boston Burglar'. Mr. Gilhouley!" Wild clapping and loud voices. Mr. Gilhouley remained obstinately squatted. "I'm still after clearin' me t'roat," he said, drinking hugely.

It went on the whole darkening evening. Every time someone opened the door we could hear the heavy-booted wind running madly across the heather and the hills, and the sea bumping outside the harbour.

A rosy, cosy lady sang 'The Wild Colonial Boy', the young girl with the penny whistle performed a sad solo which, she said, she had been practising in the rocks all day, once having tripped over a boulder, thrusting the whistle painfully up her nose. Dermot remembered some verses he had left out of 'When I was a lad in the Kerry Hills...' and recited the whole thing again. Mr. Gilhouley never got to doing 'The Boston Burglar', but remained resolutely on the floor clearin' his t'roat.

Yes, it was a fine evening at O'Regan's. Unfortunately I couldn't find my way home. I was staying with the family of Cornelius O'Donoghue, at the far end of the island, three miles of stony path over the hump of a mountain. It was only four hundred feet high, really, so it was hardly a full-grown mountain. It just seemed like a mountain. Full of the sort of desperate cheer that draught Guinness adds to an adventure, I rummaged among the boats on the beach, looking for the beginning of the hill path.

Earlier that evening, when I had walked to O'Regan's, it was vaguely foggy, but the late wind had despatched it and left behind the darkest night in which I had ever walked. There was not a hanging star nor a shine on the sea. The mountain and the sky fell upon each other like black wrestlers locked in a hold; and there was I staggering over mooring ropes and anchors, looking for the beginnings of my road home.

Just as I was convinced that the rotten Irish had moved it, I found it hiding behind a fishing boat. Yes, this was the way up and over the mountain; this was the way to the house of Cornelius O'Donoghue.

Four paces up the path and I fell into a substantial hole. I rested there, climbed out and climbed again. How do you walk such a mountain in the blackest dark, I asked myself.

The answer came. I had gone up one small bundle of a hill, and dipped down again, and was looking dismally into the great maw of the night again, when the whole side of the mountain was illuminated. Path and boulder, hole and bend, were, for a moment picked out in brightest light.

The Fastnet Lighthouse, materialising, for me, from years of impersonal weather forecasts, was sitting courageously out to sea, flashing its splendid beam over the Atlantic and, every few seconds, throwing it up the flank of Clear Isle, showing me the way to my bed at O'Donoghue's.

I had never been shown home by lighthouse light before. It was childishly adventurous and warmed my spirit. Every stone, every crouching hole, every bramble and bend, were clearly picked out in the wide, white light, before the dark swooped in again. I thought that any timid animal in the heather must be experiencing a very disturbed night. Towards the top of the hill (I conferred on it only the rank of a hill now) the wind came through and flapped about me. There were some houses up there, near the church, hunched in their own darkness. I had gone over the ridge now, over the top, and the Fastnet Light was back beyond my shoulder and no longer showing my way.

The church, which was half-way, like a cheerful slice of cream cake in the day, was a big shrouded thing at this dark hour. I could feel the corrugated path descending now. Deprived of 70,000 candlepower I was groping and uncertain again. Something shivered by me in the thick darkness, a night cat probably, scuttling along a wall. On this side of the hill the wind was like a thin man whining, not a blowing fat man as it was before. There was, I knew, still a mile and more to go to the house by the seashore where the O'Donoghue family had left the door unlatched for me.

I stopped and stood, the travelling salt in my face, the breathing of the sea coming from the unseen channel. Where was the house? Over there, that way surely, where the island seemed tired of its high existence and ran away swiftly to the crashing ocean. Then I *knew* where the house was! I *knew* the place I had to go! For Cornelius O'Donoghue, old sailor that he was, had left a navigation light for me. He had put a candle in the window.

It seemed a whole country away, between me and it a huge anonymous place brimming with darkness. But it was there, a splinter steady, small and bright, and it guided me home.

I went, the Guinness now reasserting itself over my previously doubting spirit. I walked, trotted and even ran a bit downhill, always going towards the flame in the window. I sang snatches all the way:

> Home, boys, home,
> That's where I want to be.
> Home for a while in the Ould Count-ery.

And:

> Her hair hung over her shoulder,
> Tied up with a black velvet band . . .

Several lines I remembered from 'When I was a boy in the Kerry Hills . . .' and I patched up the rest. And, when the lovely little light of the candle was very near, I recited loudly:

> How far is it to Babylon?
> Three score miles and ten.
> Can I get there by candle-light?
> Yes, and back again.

Well, it wasn't Babylon, but it was a farm. And striding triumphantly towards the door over the last field of the journey, I walked straight into the duck pond.

* * *

Only the Irish, I thought on the day I went to Clear Isle, could call the place by that name when you couldn't see it for fog. Fat banks of fog were trundling in from the Atlantic, covering the archipelago of islands that reach out from the south-west toe of Ireland. With a certain politeness, however, it stopped short and stood around just outside the harbour at Baltimore on the mainland.

There was a cheerful little fishing boat at the quay. The morning was close and languid, the flagstones of the jetty shining and wet, and the town indistinct behind the harbour. The water was like rolled lead and hardly reflected the white bellies of the gulls. They mooned across it calling with all the urgency of a yawn.

"Captain," I shouted to the man on the box of a bridge, "are you going to Clear Isle?" One thing I've learned in my island journeys is always to call the man nearest the wheel 'Captain', even if he only looks eleven years old or is eighty and wearing a straw boater. On a small boat someone will always look up and answer you, even if it is not the man at the wheel, and then at least you know where you are.

The man at the wheel, on this boat, was not the captain, but a head poked out of a hole in the deck and answered me immediately.

"I'm the captain, sor," he said. Then nodding to the helmsman: "He's the mate. There only bein' two of us, he's got no choice, you understand."

I was glad we had that sorted out. I repeated my question about Clear Isle and he thought that it was extremely likely that they would be sailing in that direction, just as long as they didn't miss it altogether in the fog.

Half an hour later we went like a whisper out of Baltimore harbour, sliding through the fog. We stole upon a quartet of seals sitting around a table of rock looking as though they were engrossed in a hand of poker. They looked up as we moved by, but briefly, and then went back to the bidding. Marooned cormorants stretched their snaked necks. Other birds occupied themselves in solitary places, the sea and the calm fog moving around them.

It was like voyaging below ground in some sibilant cavern. The captain and mate argued quietly and I stood on the wet deck and felt once more the mystery and the glad loneliness that is found in these places of the sea.

We chugged from one fog bank and into a clear alley of ocean and sky, and for a while, to port, we could see Sherkin Island, the lower finger of the elongated cape of islands. Flat to the side of the boat's wheelhouse was a sticker which said 'Murphy's Stout — The Greatest' which was comforting. It reminded me of the crisps sticker John Dennison carried on his wheelhouse a thousand miles from here in the Orkneys.

Another forest of fog caught us, engulfed us, but when we were out of that the sea swept out clear and clean to the horizon. A grin of sunshine came through and there was Clear Isle — the Irish logic exonerated — all brown and summer purple across its broad hill. There were cottages on the cliffs' edges, like sitting men, pensive, fishing.

We sidled by some low islets, bonneted with green and supporting families of gulls and cormorants, and then went wide around a single snout of rock that was blowing white water like an Antarctic whale.

There was no sign of a harbour; on islands there rarely is until the last moment, until the final protecting rock is rounded. But I knew it would not be far, for the familiar roundabout of gulls turned behind the high rocks confronting us, and that was where the harbour was hidden.

The boat sniffed around the rocks and panted into the land-locked pool like a dog pleased to have rediscovered a familiar rabbit-hole. The mist had retreated across the sea now and sat at a respectful distance in the vicinity of the Fastnet Rock. The Irish sun, one eye open, looked down on the harbour. The boat wrinkled the water as we made for the stone jetty. There was a fishing boat tied there, striped and coloured, and a few people leaning on things watching us coming in.

Our huffing noise bounced gently from the high rocks and the higher hills that cupped the harbour. A sense of delight stole over me as I knew, gradually realised, what a marvellous place this was. Three pubs squatted at intervals of a few yards up the path from the jetty. They are known locally as the Stations of the Cross. A fallen church, its tombstones stuck this way and that, listing and heeling like ships, was set on a mound at the back of the harbour, and a tethered donkey cropped the grass around the feet of a white statue of The Virgin.

The harbour had another arm, a basin beautiful with many-coloured mud, the hulls of two old boats, and gulls conversing on its iron railings. A house, the colour of dark cheese, was at the head of this basin, the mild sun giving it a superb richness and throwing its fine reflection into the half-tide water below it. It is used now as a bird observatory, and the pop records being played that morning by the young bird observers suddenly issued across the quiet harbour and frightened all the birds away.

Clear Isle was a good island. You could tell that by the sense of isolated well-being in the morning air; by the way the hedgerows were thick and sparkling with little August flowers; by the slow way the people moved and the donkeys grazed; by the indolence of the dogs and the look of amusement on the faces of the fat cats. Doors were open in the satisfied walls of cottages, and in the front of O'Regan's pub.

Bill O'Regan said they didn't have room to put me up as they were expecting, any day, a party of drunks from the mainland. On the other hand he thought that the house of Cornelius O'Donoghue might suit me very well, although it was at the other end of the island where the hills flattened out against the sea, and a good walk from the nearest bar, which happened to be his. If I liked he would give me a lift to the cross-roads as he had to go that way to drop the nurse's children off and talk to a man who was going to a funeral.

I involved myself willingly in this package deal and we set off up the track in his morbid Morris, dropping the children off with the nurse (who was feeding her chickens), going to see the bereaved man, and finally arriving at the cross-roads.

Only in Ireland, and probably only in an island of Ireland (and one with six cars at that) would you come to a point where two single-track roads meet, neither of them more than seven feet wide, and be confronted with an official road sign ordering you to Halt and Beware of Other Traffic. Bill O'Regan showed me the O'Donoghue's house basking by the sea a mile away across the velvet fields.

O'Regan had been away from Clear Isle for twenty years, like many others have been away, but he had gone back to take on the pub and the grocery store that was in with it. He didn't think he would be moving again.

I left him at the cross-roads, promising to be over at his pub in the evening "for the singin'" and humped my bag down the sheepish meadows, along the cowed lanes, towards the house by the ocean.

The sun, now awake and working well, was lying all along the coast of Cork across the wide, racing straits, turning the far hills golden and lighting up the southern towns. Between O'Donoghue's house and that mainland there was a whole flotilla of small islands straddled along the channel. Some were topped with green, others black with rock and white with birds. All had their own bow-wave as the Atlantic ran about them so that they were ships pushing on some frustrating voyage that never went anywhere.

There was a pond in the field outside the O'Donoghue's

front door, there were two giant hooded crows sitting on his gateposts and looking truculent. So I went around the back, navigated several cows and a mule, and called down into the house with my back to the sea.

Seven faces came to the door at my voice. "Is Mr. Cornelius O'Donoghue there?" I shouted again, like a court usher calling a witness. It was quite windy there above the sea and I felt I needed to shout.

"He is!" replied all seven faces at once.

There was a prolonged pause. The cows shifted and the mule looked at me with some disdain. The hooded crows rose from the front gate and cawed lustily a hundred feet over my head as though they'd never heard such a lot of human noise.

"Mister O'Regan sent me," I called. "From the pub."

"What did he send you with?" said a man's voice.

"Can you put me up?" I hollered. "He said you could."

"We can too," said a small man detaching himself from the anonymity of the doorway. "If you'll be so kind as to come down."

The mule sniffed audibly but the crows had stopped cawing and were just hovering now, witnessing the scene. I went down the scant path and climbed over the wall into the back garden. Now the crowd at the door broke up and came out enthusiastically to see me. Cornelius was a small man and his wife was a big woman. He was a sailor turned farmer, with a weathered, wise face. Every time I saw him he seemed to be cutting something with a penknife.

"Cornelius O'Donoghue," he said putting his penknife in the other hand and shaking hands with me. "And this is Mrs. Ellen O'Donoghue." She had a big round face, very pleasant and steamy.

"Miss Nora Driscoll." An old lady.

"Miss Mary Cadogan." Another old lady.

Sheep shearing by the Auskerry lighthouse. The author is on the left

The Ocean Mountain— Skellig Michael from the air

Blasket boatmen carrying their curragh

Beehive huts on Skellig Michael.
Little Skellig is in the
background

In harbour at Clear Isle

Old Patrick Driscoll of Clear Isle

*Water patterns between
Herm and Jethou*

Irene MacLachan—
living alone on Luing

schoolteacher Jane Waters
r daughter Caroline—
er cent of her school

'Clinker' and the baby seal

"Mr. Patrick Driscoll." An old man with a half a pipe. "I'm seventy-nine," he said.

"Master Patrick O'Donoghue." A little lad. "I'm eight," he said.

Cornelius looked around as though to see if there were any more. "My daughters are absent at the moment of speakin'," he apologised.

"So you've come to stay with us," he said when we were in the house. There was a stone floor and wooden furniture, pictures of Christ, the Pope, and the late President Kennedy, some pokerwork rhymes amd mottoes, and a fine dresser hung with dazzling crockery. "I'll tell you this," he continued, "you're the second from across the water who's come to stay in this house in a few weeks, and it's never happened before. I t'ink that United Nations must be doin' some good after all." He showed me to my room with a candle by my bed. "One way and another," he smiled, "it's a great day for this house. Come, I'll show you something."

They had, that day, got water from a tap for the first time. Cornelius had laid some pipes from the well and connected them to a single tap sticking like a gun from a wall in the kitchen.

"Look at that," he said. With a flourish he turned the tap. Nothing happened. All the people of the house were gathered frowning and worried. Cornelius gave the tap a bang. Out came the water, cold and gushing. Moses, when he struck the desert rock with his staff and attained the same success, was never more pleased.

*　　*　　*

Cornelius had been a sailor. "All over," he nodded. "Gulf of Mexico, South America, up in the Arctic. But I've come back. Everybody seems to come back."

O'Regan had returned after twenty years. Cornelius was home, so were many of the others on that island. There were men there who knew Bilboa, Montevideo, Houston, and Port Everglades, but had never been to Dublin. They agreed that that little toe of Ireland, its dampness, its greenness, the fog and the curious habit of the sea vanishing before your eyes, had a special voice that called them to return. Sometimes they returned to settle, to slow up from the whirl of the world, sometimes to die, and sometimes they were too late even for that.

They tell the tale of the Clear Islander who, about to die on the Irish mainland, asked his two good friends to take him to the island for burial and requested that they keep his grave decent and tidy. They agreed, took him in a little boat across the strait, buried him, and returned the next spring to carry out the second part of their vow. They stood, one each side of the small hump in the ground, lost for once for words. Seamus had the garden clippers and Brendan the trowel. Someone had to break the silence. "Aye," said Seamus, "he's got a fine first growth."

Nora Driscoll had returned too. She came in and sat at the wooden table when I was at the house and said: "They laugh at me now. I'm after forgettin' the Gaelic, you see. Half the time I don't know what they're goin' on about." She nodded towards the rest of the family in the kitchen. "Fifty-five years in the United States of America, and just come home." She said it '*You*-nitedstates', but fifty-five years or not her accent was the slow, damp voice of the Clear Islander. "Sixteen when I left," she said. "I was born in that cottage up there on the brow. You see it. Cost me fifteen pound in those days to go to the United States. Never been back till now. It's very strange this island. They've got the gas here now. Ah. . . . Progress, progress."

Patrick Driscoll had gone back to the island too. Not the old man, Patrick Driscoll who lived with the O'Donoghues, but another man who had been a sailor and who lived just up the field. This is Driscoll country. O'Driscoll, the raider, built his castle on the west of Clear Isle and they're all his family.

Patrick's house had been in ruins for forty years. When he came back from the sea in his forties, a bachelor looking for a home, he walked along the thick lane and stood looking at the place. The top had fallen through, weeds were climbing out of the windows, it was easier to get in through the roof than through the door. The few fields around were high with grass and nettles, the outbuildings were just piles of stone and the gates like ancient skeletons.

"But a man needs a place to be his own, to have just some personal ground to stand on," said Patrick. The bones of his face were sharp under his red skin. He had blue eyes, intelligent, perceptive. He was working by his barn one evening when we talked. His voice was quietly poetic. There were cows in his fields, chickens about the place, and a good slate roof on the house. "When you travel, like a sailor," he said, "every place in the earth becomes the same. You need one place to be different from the others, and this is the different place for me."

He bought the smallholding, rebuilt the house and the barn with great industry and skill, tilled the fields, bought his stock, and every now and then walked down to the sea to watch the ocean ships going past.

The house was finished and painted white. There was a tub of flowers at the door and dogs barking. But Patrick has remained alone. When the mist moves about the island at night he sits in his kitchen, the fire warming the stone flags, and plays his piano accordion to himself and his dog. I heard him as I went by, very late from O'Regan's, still playing, the fire colouring the window. "I may go to sea again," he told me. "I don't settle easily. But this will always be mine. I'll have somewhere different to any other place that I wander."

*   *   *

Clear Isle is shaped like a rising fish, with the harbour and O'Regan's, and the other pubs at the point where the stout body joins the tail fin. Apart from the settlement around the harbour there is no acknowledged village; the cottages and the smallholdings spaced and spread about like they are on Fair Isle in the remote north. But every district has its name, Ballyieragh, Knockanacohig, Knockanna-mauragh, Comillane and Keenleen, even though it may be just another hill or glen, with stones and heather and nomad sheep. Apart from the small valleys in the centre of the island you can see the ocean from everywhere, and in the ocean the heads and shoulders of many small shoals and islets.

O'Driscoll's Castle stands up like a big bad tooth on a headland called Coosadoona, where the famed Irish pirate could see promising cargoes coming over the trade routes. It's a decayed, hollow place now, its rugged days over, with the everlasting waves still sounding below its stones.

South-west of that, going down towards the tail of the fish is a lake, a small lough like a dull coin caught in the cupped palm of half a dozen small hills. It was a day of low clouds and bunches of showers when I went to the lough. It looked dead and cold with sharp corrugations running across it. The hills were reflected as smudges and birds of various families stood in depressed, one-legged, groups, around its mud.

The sea is ever grand, raging dark or clean with sunshine. It always has something to give, something to display, whether it be stormy excitement or warm contentment. Birds and waves are always on the move. It can never be dull. But fresh water, especially enclosed like the little lough on Clear Isle, needs a blue sky. Otherwise it grows cold and brittle, and lies like dead until the sun warms it again. The reeds standing at its edges were as sharp and unpicturesque as a park railing, the mud was just mud, and even a rabbit

which I found sitting vacantly on a run of grass at the water's
edge did nothing to give the place charm. I walked away
and went to have a look at the sea again.

The heather on the piles of minor hills was wet and
clinging, but I got to the top and looked out over the many-
pointed summits, then across the fields which flowed from
them like carpets on display, and then to the sea-channels,
still alive, still busy. A boat was edging between the main
island and the islets just offshore; a man rode a donkey, a
big man and a small donkey, as always, along the main path
that traversed the island. But apart from the interruptions of
seabirds there was nothing else moving and the only sound
was that of a mild grey breeze from the south-west.

When I had reached the path and was walking on there
were added sounds. Beside the way was a hidden stream
moving along secretly over stones and ridges beneath the
brambles and thick blackberry bushes. It tapped away
industriously like a typewriter. You half expected to hear a
ding at the end of each line. Then a distant donkey started
braying over the hedges. It is a quiet island and it was a loud
donkey. He honked dramatically like someone with a big
cold in a huge nose, the sound horning across the land
causing some geese to pass comment and even getting raised
eyebrows from the cows eating the meadows by the road.

There was an old lighthouse on the top horizon to my
right, its eyes gone blind, its body crumbling as the sea and
the wind got their gradual own-back. It was half-gone now,
its outline short like the stump of a felled tree.

I went by the well, from which Cornelius and other island
men were now piping the water to their kitchens. Some one-
tap kitchen units of metal and plastic were coming over on
the boat any day, it was told. Houses were grouped closer
together at the north-western part of the island — at the
fish's mouth end. There were wedged inlets up there called
Coosnaesk, Coosadouglas, Coosecoppal and Cooslahan,

their little capes pointing out to a scattering of skerries called Carrigmore.

At Coosadouglas there is a landing place. A young jetty is sheltered by some mature cliffs so that, even on the roughest days the water is safe for manœuvring a small boat. There was no one down there that morning. The sun had come out for a while and it was warm in that enclosed place. There were some rowing boats pulled up out of the water, some lobster pots on the flat rock behind the jetty, and two pairs of boots and three old raincoats stored under a ledge by the Clear Isle fishermen.

I sat against the rump of the jetty, my face to the sun, my feet thrust out in the general direction of Skibbereen. What happened next was quite strange. I had been thinking about something Cornelius had told me the evening before. We had walked down the lane from his cottage to the sea and he showed me the place across the rocky beach where, 120 years ago, a telegraph cable had gone across to the Irish mainland.

"There's a little house over by the coastguard cottages, not a great way from the lough," he said. "And that was the cable station. The sailin' ships sailin' from America would fire a gun when they were goin' by Cape Clear and the men of the island would row out to them and pick up a buoy, and in the buoy were the dispatches and the news from America. They'd bring it ashore and then take it to the cable station. In no time it would be tapped off to Dublin and then to London, while it took the sailin' ship another three days or more to get to England.

"This place, mister, might not be the centre o' the universe now, but it was the first spot in the Old World to hear about the end of the American Civil War."

I was thinking of that when I saw something blue floating in the green water below, flopping against the ribs of the jetty. It was a blue book like the London S to Z telephone directory. I leaned over and fished it out. It was a Directory of Ship Stations, a wireless code book used by radio men at sea, listing nations, vessels and their call-signs.

Carefully I separated the wet pages. I learned that the code for the British Solomon Islands Protectorate is SLM, that TMP is Portuguese Timor, if I should ever want to call it, and I'd have no trouble at all with the Oriental Republic of Uruguay — just URG.

Then I checked on individual ships. I can now contact, if I wish, the captain of the French fishing vessel *Gisele et Guy* (or at least the radio officer, and I could ask him to go and get the captain); I know the call-sign for the Hungarian ship *Magyarorszag* (the first time I had realised that the Hungarians have ships) and I can also get in touch with *Senorita Cecilia II* (although she's usually round about the Philippines, so it would need to be a good line).

I could have played for hours like this but for the arrival of a small boat. It swooped with the swift tide, coming around the headland like a hare around a greyhound track, running quickly in to the mooring. Three island men were aboard. They'd been fishing and had come back with a boatload of pollack. Another man, older, long and thin and all in the island black, with a little girl, came down and took some fish from the men, fixing them on a hook through their mouths and gills.

With him and the girl I walked up the path again. He was another wanderer returned home to Clear Isle. It seems that they all go back. Back from the sun and the cities, the ports estuaries and oceans of the world. Back to this damp little place where nothing happens but the weather. "How long were you away from the island?" I asked him as we walked. He had given the fish to the little girl and she swung them on the hook.

"Fifteen years," he said. "Far away."

Another sailor, another roamer, I thought, sitting in his cottage at dead of night thinking of Singapore, Jakarta and the Indies.

"Where is 'Far away'?" I asked.

"Birmingham," he said.

"In Memory of our Beloved Parrot"

Going over the sea to these small islands I have voyaged with several sorts of men and some odd cargo. At different times I have shared a deck with three distinct breeds of sheep, dogs, cats, a pigeon; a Ministry of Works hut (pre-fabricated); Mr. T. Watson Forgie, retired cathedral organist who tunes island pianos; casks of Guinness; bales of hay; a sea-sick monk; sober lighthouse men; Mr. Roy Dennis, who has seen the famous Arctic owl of Fetlar, starched nurses, starchy bread, bottles of pop, and a man who had run away from Wandsworth. The borough, not the prison.

I have helped to put a four-year-old French girl on a potty, on deck, in the teeth of a force nine gale. I have sung Irish rebel songs with a curly young renegade from Tipperary. I have seen tears travel through salt spray on an old woman's face because she was travelling home.

Going to Herm was a shorter journey than most. On deck were boxes of Lyons biscuits (dainty tea), canisters of washing powder, a man with a gun after rabbits, and two others who were going to try to mend a tractor which had broken down on the edge of a cliff. It was only three miles across the neck of a channel between the little island and Guernsey. But a bull-headed wind was tearing through the strait, lopping the tops from the green waves. Sudden squalls came like raiders, soaked us, and howled away again. Mustard-coloured clouds foamed over the dark land and the irritable sea.

Herm is a quaint little boat of an island. Sailing alongside those grand galleons of summer, Jersey and Guernsey, it gets uncomfortably caught in their wash. In the good weather months the visitors clamber over it, explore it along its short length, picnic and boil kettles, lose children, and skim back to the big islands in the evenings. Thousands do it at seven shillings per head. But by October they have all done and gone, and Herm is left peaceful for winter.

This was October, with an autumn wind and sea, but spaces of good sunshine, and an empty island waiting to be walked. Its bevelled back rises almost immediately from its shore line, but not high and not bleak. Trees were patterned on the top ledge against the sun as I got ashore from the boat, and the thick gorse and heather was turning a rich brown like the changing coat of a country animal.

It was worth looking back at the sea from the jetty. St. Peter Port over the channel was glistening with violent sun after rain. The sea was chopped to pieces by the hard wind, spray and spume flying from the splendid green. Sitting grumpily in the middle of it all was a dour Martello Tower, set as a chesspiece among all the confusion. There were reefs and islets close inshore, like hats and hands and noses sticking out of the waves, and beyond them the handsome head of the island of Jethou.

It was on this jetty in 1945 that Major Alexander Gough Wood, a New Zealander known as Peter, came ashore to begin a life as ruler of Herm. He took a sixty-six-year lease of the island from the Balliwick of Guernsey and he is still there. He relates that two minutes after he and his wife stepped ashore on the jungled island, powerfully overgrown through wartime neglect, they passed a man walking towards the sea.

"Good morning," said the Major.

"Good morning," said the man, not turning his head but walking on.

"We never saw him again," said the Major. "He did not get off the island by any boat from the jetty. We still don't know who he was."

Placed as it was in the wet no-man's-land between Occupied France and Britain, sitting sweating between the island garrisons of Jersey and Guernsey, Herm experienced a unique and frequently comedic war. Lord Perry, who leased the isle up to 1940 (and who painted everything that could be painted, including the Herm lorry, in his racing colours of blue and orange) left a man called Kemp as caretaker at the onset of the war. One lovely shimmering morning in 1940 Kemp heard that the German armies were in St. Malo and anxiously sailed the island boat across to Guernsey to find out what was going on. At St. Peter Port he met an old friend called Dickson and, on impulse, asked him if he would 'keep an eye on Herm for a few days'.

Dickson agreed and Kemp took him across to the isle, left him, and returned with the only boat to Guernsey.

Within the next couple of days the marooned Dickson, sitting comfortably on the two-hundred-foot knob of Monks Hill on Herm had a superbly untrammelled view of the German conquest of Guernsey. When eventually the explosions stopped and the smoke had drifted with the channel wind a party of Germans came across to the island.

The officer in charge turned out to be an amateur geologist and he spent that morning mysteriously foraging about for lumps of stone. Then he suggested that Dickson should remain in occupation and promised to send Mrs. Dickson across by the first available boat.

This was done and the couple lived on Herm, an accidental King and Queen, throughout the years of occupation. They lived in Lord Perry's house, guarded jealously his stocked and stacked wine cellar, and cleaned his silver regularly. Once a party of Wehrmacht officers sailed across and tried to get hold of the silver. Dickson complained to the German authorities and to his astonishment Colonel Knackfuss, from Jersey, arrived, stayed a couple of days and caught one of his own officers in the act of lifting the silver. In front of Dickson the Colonel tore the young man's epaulettes from his jacket and sent him off to somewhere where a soldier's life was more complicated.

Later Dickson thought his little land was to be occupied in earnest, for troops were brought across from Guernsey and a swoop of invasion barges came in on the summer waves to the long Shell Beach at the north-east corner of Herm. There was a lot of noise, explosions and shooting. Dickson crept over and found a full-cry battle going on which was being energetically filmed by German cameramen. The result was later shown in the Fatherland's cinemas under the title 'The Invasion of the Isle of Wight'.

At one time the occupation army established an anti-aircraft battery on Herm. It shot down only one aeroplane — one of its own fighter-bombers — which crashed spectacularly on Shell Beach. Shamefaced, the gunners were withdrawn.

But the epic of Dickson's reign came when he complained about soldiers who started gorse fires while romping with girls or shooting pheasant on Herm. He nailed a notice prohibiting smoking to the jetty so that every German soldier could see it. This piece of law-enforcement was accepted by most, but so enraged a colonel of artillery that he returned to Guernsey, ordered his men to their guns, and opened up on Herm with a shuddering bombardment. It was concentrated on the northern common of the island where there was nothing to kill but rabbits, but it gave Mr. and Mrs. Dickson a nasty hour or so. The craters are still there.

The war proceeded very near, but oddly far away. Herm had occasional visitors, including a clergyman from Guernsey who was regularly machine-gunned by British and American fighter aircraft as he sailed across to the island. A party of British commandos turned up one dark night, had cups of tea from Mrs. Dickson and went away again.

In the glad early summer of 1945 Herm was liberated, the total German occupation army at that time being one German Baron who had been exiled there as a suspect in a plot to assassinate Vice Admiral Huffmeier, the Nazi Commander-in-Chief of the Channel Islands. The nobleman, Baron Von Helldorf, had planned to eliminate his chief as the Vice Admiral was drinking his morning milk, but the plot went wrong. Von Helldorf was sent across to Herm with his belongings and was on the beach to meet the liberating allies when they went ashore.

The day I arrived on Herm, Major Wood was away, but his accountant, John Stringer, with a shotgun under his elbow came down to the jetty. He explained that when he is not adding figures he is generally subtracting from the rabbit population. He also has the key to the island pub — the Mermaid. "Sometimes in the winter," he said, "one of the estate workers fancies a pint, so I go up and unlock the bar. I buy him one and he buys me one, then I lock up again."

There was spray leaping across the jetty every time a

green wave blew up on the rocks below. When the sun came out it coloured the fragments, making a minor rainbow. "Wild today," said John Stringer. We waited for the next throw of the sea and, after it had gone, made a run for the dry-land side of the jetty.

There was a tidy half-street of cottages with a lamp-post upright among them, October flowers ducking under the tops of walls, and, above us the gigantic swaying of the channel wind among the top trees. It was a good place to turn and look at the sea. What a *thing* the sea is! What a creature, compelling attention, admiration, exhilaration in any or all of its moods. It was thrashing wild about the island now, the full sweep of the gale, blowing over sheltering Guernsey, finally swooping like a roller coaster, flinging it up. It was green and crested in the open reach of Little Russell. There is a big hole in the rock of Pierre Percee — they say they used to chain mermaids there and sell them — and the sea was leaping up and trying to climb through. Then it soared, thick and fine with the sun flying over it, in the strait between Herm and Jethou. There were no boats out today. The sea had the place to itself.

I walked with John Stringer along the thin road that reaches towards the southern butt of the island. He nodded towards the little crane standing on the jetty, its neck necking forward like an obedient servant awaiting orders. "Hundred and fifty years old, that crane," said John. "Still works fine. They brought it here in the old days when they were quarrying on the island. They've carted some rock from here, believe me. Half the island is spread around the world. The Duke of York's Steps in London came from the top of the hill over there."

We approached a dwarfish building, round with a bullet-headed roof. It recalled for me the little sheep-house standing in the debris of the village on Great Blasket.

"A prison," said John. "Not in the Wormwood Scrubbs

class, but a nick nevertheless. They built it here so that any of the quarrymen who got too drunk could be thrown in there to cool off. It's very strong of course. Built of the best Herm granite."

The day fell dark and blowy for a while, then the sun came sailing beautifully across the sea like a golden ship. Birds jumped from the cliffs and rocks and rose to meet it, dancing in the bright wind.

John Stringer began to work his way down the rocks. "The tide is right for the ormers," he called. "Come down." There was bladderwrack and bubbled seaweed draped over the boulders; there were dripping drops and concealed pools, each a wild acquarium. I picked my way down until the big stones became fewer, until they sat singly widely spaced on the smaller shingle like well-padded winter anglers do on desolate beaches.

"Ormers," said John, tugging at a rock square as a tombstone, "are the speciality of Herm. Here's one stuck under this."

The ormer turned out to be a lazy limpet about four fat inches across, which seemed to yawn with boredom as he pulled it from its perch. "They're always just under the rocks, sitting where the sea can wash them," John went on. "You can collect a bucketful in no time. You prise them out of the shell, which is no bother, and then, because they're a bit tough you bash them with a hammer to soften the meat up. Then you cook them. They're very tasty."

I said I wasn't keen on sea-food, especially the sort you bash with a hammer. We found other ormers secretly snoring under other nuggets of rock, but we had nothing in which to collect them so we spared them the hammer and left them to enjoy the wash of another tide.

We went back towards the jetty and then I went alone, climbing the narrow arched lane up and across the waist of the island. The way was covered with well-nourished trees, ash and rowan and flashing silver birch, thrashing above in the streaming wind, making their wonderful sweeping, weeping noise. Below, crowding the sides of the lane, were tousled blackberry bushes, brilliant with ripe fruit, and lower still tiny diffident weeds and sheltering flowers fearful of the change in the weather.

The first evidence of human ingenuity I found on this windy walk was a memorial in stone to a parrot. The blackberries have used it as a convenient aid to climbing, but as memorials to parrots go, it wasn't bad. It looked like a dignified fountain, but without water, and immortalises a bird owned by Lord Perry which swore once too often at some drunken sailors and was promptly strangled for its rudeness.

Animals have always had a bad time on Herm. Prince Blucher von Wahlsatt, a nineteenth-century owner of the island, introduced wallabies and they flourished and increased. Then the prince's chef and butler, during their employer's absence of course, went out for a day's hunting and shot all but two of the creatures. They did a month in prison for their sport. It seems likely, however, that some wallabies survived on Herm for years because a sentry of the South Staffordshire Regiment stationed there in 1915 was observed running from his post in some terror and reported to his orderly officer that he had been "attacked by a perishin' kangaroo".

The path, with its guardian trees, reached, at its highest, the middle settlement of Herm, the chapel, the manor house, some low cottages, and a farm. Major Wood's peaceful house is there too, a friendly-fronted house with a deep walled garden.

He says that after the wartime neglect it took three weeks to hack a way through the overgrowth to reach the front door. He is now, by all accounts, a contented man, and it looks a contented man's house. In summer it must appear fine in the island sun, and even today, this rough-edged day in autumn, it had about it a sense of grave satisfaction.

A dappled horse was nibbling a field just over the hedge as though he had all day, which he probably had. There, I thought, is a Robinson Crusoe of a horse; an animal that has known no streets, no smoke, no mainland noise. A horse with the sea in his veins, cropping salty grass, and being ridden sometimes along cliff-top and across the flat spread of a beach at low tide.

Sir Compton Mackenzie, another of Herm's rulers, once lived in the stone box of a manor up there on the back of the island. He called it the ugliest building in Europe. It has, I think, now been surpassed in London, several times in fact, but it is certainly no beauty. Today it looked sullen too, with the trees banging against its battlements and one of its pointed windows flying loose, to and fro, as though a whole succession of ghosts were jumping out in a hurry.

The serene little chapel is up here too. It has geraniums on its window ledges and a bell with a becoming note housed like a hermit in a separate belfry in the church garden. The church has been there in some form since the fifteenth century. It is dedicated to St. Tugual, rumoured to be a Welsh woman put to death by the Saxons. Since, however, this saint was, on the threadbare evidence, the travelling companion of St. Magloire on his journey to Herm it seems unlikely that St. Tugual was a woman, Welsh or otherwise. Not unless they've changed the rules since then. The small church is hallowed and cosy as a sea-shell. Major Wood holds simple services there as long as there is someone on the island who can play the organ. Holidaying clergymen are asked to celebrate Communion, and sometimes they are lucky and get a bishop.

The island school of Herm is the end cottage of a delicate row. It has two pupils. One is the four-year-old daughter of the teacher.

Jane Waters runs the school. She is a dark, happy, young woman, expecting her third child when I went to see her. "You could say I'm making sure of my future," she laughed. "Caroline represents fifty per cent of the school strength now. I've got James, who is nine months, and the new one arriving soon. Everyone thinks I'm trying to stock up."

Paul, her husband, is one of the estate gardeners on the island. They left Sussex for Herm and they say they are very glad. "It's strange," said Jane Waters, "to have letters and circulars addressed to you as 'The Principal' or 'The Head Teacher' of Herm School. It's a very different school, of course. We only open in the mornings and I fix the holidays when I like. We had school throughout August so that I can take some time off when I have the next baby."

The other half of the school is five-year-old Clare Stringer, John's daughter. "But we've calculated that within a few years we will have a school population of eight," said Jane. She rubbed some jam from James's face. We walked up two steps into the schoolroom. Two miniature desks, and the coloured letters, numbers and pictures of every infant school bright on the walls. Over the age of eleven the children of Herm have to go to a boarding school in Guernsey.

"The children are pretty advanced," said Jane. Caroline, a busy, talkative four-year-old, agreed and wrote her name and age on a piece of paper to bear out the point. Her mother said: "But I play it a lot by ear. If it's sunny we go out of doors, if it rains we're tucked in the classroom. Sometimes I give the children some task to do and I come in here and peel the potatoes. You have to adapt yourself."

I went from the cottage, across the lawn and into the road again. Seagulls were sitting on the housetop, calling their wilful call, and I thought it must be a marvellous place to go to school. Caroline came from the door and began to work the garden swing. She called out: "I'm Caroline. I'm never late for school. I'm already here!"

There's a flour mill, aching with age, at the top of the settlement, beyond the farm, and a wooden contraption like a village stocks which, a century ago, was used for shoeing oxen working on the island chores.

From this height of Herm's hump I took a sloping path, red and rain-churned, down to Belvoir Bay, a toe-nail of a beach, clean and deserted, facing, today, the side-swipe of the gale funnelling through two islet-rocks called Caquoro-bert and Putrainee. It chiselled the tops from the running waves, unrolling the muslin spume from them. The standing rocks fluted the wind so that it emerged on to the bowl of the open beach like the booming of a tuneless brass band. The gulls, as ever, enjoyed the ragged day, playing tag in the air currents, rushing and turning superbly. By contrast one ancient sea-bird, wings elegantly still and spread, floated gently down the cliff-face, remaining effortlessly horizontal, and with all the nobility of an invalid dowager in a descending lift.

The cliffs have old features here, grimacing across to the rocks of Sark, equally old, like quarrelsome grannies in confrontation. By the beach, at the bottom landing of the cliff path, is a hut which in summer sells ice-cream and trays of tea and fizzing pop. It had been left to its winter solitude, sorry-looking, and woodenly cold. Someone, last August, long ago now, had written a message on its boards. It said: 'Herm for the Hermits'.

Shell Beach, beyond a platoon of straight and steady rocks to the north, is an unrolled blanket reaching to the extremity of the island. This was the strand the Germans purloined for their film fairy tale about the invasion of the Isle of Wight. The reefs, ridges and skerries just offshore could be a frieze depicting that famous non-battle, their low forms, struggling in the sea are like petrified invaders.

At quiet days in the year, away from the summer and its people, lonely, shuffling men go along this beach, their eyes fixed on the texture of the sand, or on the little pools of sea left trapped by the rocks after the high tide. They are the conchologists, the seekers of shells, the seashore detectives looking for a rare design or a strange pearl curl. They find them here on Shell Beach, conches from deeps as distant as the Gulf of Mexico, carried in the stomach of the Gulf Stream and thrown on this little channel isle.

The northern nose of Herm used to be called Les Hommes, and its cape is still known as Pointe du Gentilhomme, but to most people it has become, unromantically, the Common. It was here that the bristling German artillery colonel aimed his high-explosive shells when he became annoyed with Dickson, the island's wartime keeper.

The bruises are still there, covered now with the yellow burnet rose, the infant of roses, and with the congregating eglantine. It was here that the ancients buried their dead and their tufty barrows sit aptly among the mounds thrown up by the artillery shells. Thousands of people were buried on Herm and, since the island up to the eighteenth century was all but barren, it seems logical that tribes from the other isles and from France must have used it as a depository for the dead, leaving a solemn few of their people ashore to see that the graves were tended or whatever they did to graves in those lost days.

It seems that the name Herm is some form of Rima, the word the Romans gave to the island, a term meaning open and barren. It is only in the last century or so, aided by piles of seaweed manure, that the bold trees of Herm, its springtime freesia, its blackberries and wild mint, have given the bald island a coat.

Standing like a clown's hat in stone at this northern stretch is a monument to nothing, which appears to be one up even on the other monument to a parrot. It's called Pierre aux Rats and was built by the granite company years ago to replace a monolith which had stood from ancient times and was always known by that name, though no one knows why. When the granite men dressed the weathered stone and shipped it to be slotted in some English railway tunnel, the Guernsey fishermen found they were bereft of the day-mark which had been used ever since sailors worked those waters. So the granite company built the present Pierre aux Rats, tidily and with some craftsmanship, and today it is marked on navigational charts so that mariners don't get lost.

In those somewhat hairy days of the quarrying they discovered copper and signs of silver on Herm. In no time five hundred men were hacking at the rocks or digging into the clay sub-soil on the island that hardly anyone had noticed since its career as a cemetery. They said that London Bridge was to be built of Herm granite. The digging and the mining went on, there were gangs and fights and wild living that would have been understood in the Klondike. But they didn't build London Bridge from the granite, and the copper gave out and the mineshafts were throttled with flood-water.

Everybody went away, leaving just awesome holes and tunnels in the ground that are there today (shouting down them is a worthwhile experience of eerieness) and a hill with its stony head chopped off.

Across that bristly common the wind flew unchecked and very strong; I had to lean into it to walk and even the burnet rose, midget though it is, lay flat under the long-running gusts.

By the pathside, going back towards the village and the jetty, I found two stubby tombstones, hiding together, overgrown and with the inscriptions rubbed thin by the years of weather. They formally record the burial of K. W. Conden, aged two years, and R. Mansfield, thirty-three years, who died of cholera aboard a ship in the strait in 1832. The granite men buried them and stood up the stones, although anyone who could call a toddler 'K. W. Conden' couldn't have cared a lot.

Back at the jetty they were counting the day's bag of rabbits. It was not much. "They don't like the wind," said one man. "It's best to sleep over here," said another, "and get 'em in the half-light while they're jumping about in the grass." John Stringer came down to the jetty to say goodbye. He and the others on Herm had a long winter of clearing and painting and mending before the boats of another visitors' summer arrive.

But they must feel content and isolated on Herm, in their houses in the ocean, warm all the stormy winter; waiting for the flowered spring and the sun. I think I would like the waiting better than the summer.

A Hawk in the Sky

It was full autumn now with the hills bald, brown, bronze when the sun came out, and the sea blue and icy. At Oban obese seabirds sat on the mud waiting for the fishing boats to come in; waiting for dinner. The steamer for the islands was taking on cargo at the pier. It was a quiet day and nobody hurried.

Tommy Ross took me in his taxi from the town and down to a bridge across the Atlantic — where the ocean is whittled to a channel — to the Isle of Seil and then to get the boat for Luing. We passed the inn called Tigh-and-Truish, the House of the Trousers, where the modest men from the Hebrides used to change their kilts for trousers on their journeys to the mainland cities.

Luing, they call it 'Ling', but somehow you can still hear the 'u', is the most inner of the Inner Hebrides, cosseted and shielded by an escort of smaller isles, by the mass of Mull to the north-west and the elegant bulk of Jura to the south. Lying across the channel from Seil it looked modestly hilly and comfortable, with two white houses at its landing stage and black hooded crows hovering high with a light wind in the clear air.

Donald MacDougal took me across in the grey boat. Two currents, sweeping in and mixing, caught us in the middle of the short crossing and quarrelled around the boat, but they were always fighting like that, Donald said, and he was well used to it.

"Yon crows," he muttered, nodding to the circus of them moving about the forehead of Luing's first hill. "Yesterday one o' them was trying to break a winkle shell he'd picked up from the beach. He'd fly up with it and drop it and try to break it on the rocks. But he kept missing the rocks and so he couldn'a crack it. The winkle stayed inside the shell. Then yon devil took it higher up and let it go again. It went straight through the glass roof at the back o' my house. Like a wee bomb. Took me all het afternoon to get the pane put in again."

We swung into the easy landing and I got ashore. Another shore, another island; almost the end of a whole journey of islands for me. Donald was a short jaunty man. He wore an oilskin and a woolly cap. "The road goes straight up there," he pointed. "Ye'll find a wee fork to the right. Take that for the village. If ye see John Brown, my brother-in-law, working in the field tell him his tea's ready."

John Brown was scything the field. A sharp November wind was cutting around a headland and hitting his face which was cold and red. He wore an old raincoat and a beret, and was turning the scythe with a rustic ease. But he was glad to know that his tea was waiting. Although he was in the field on that day, he explained, he was, in fact, a slate quarryman, the last of generations who have cut hard slates from the steely flanks of Luing island.

"When they built the abbey on Iona, the first time, ye'll

understand, they took the slates from here. Aye, all those centuries ago. Then when they rebuilt it, a few years back, they came here and asked me for some more slates just the same as the one's they used then. They said they had to be good slates. They had to last for a thousand years. I cut the slates, down there see, by the water's edge, and sent them off and they put them on the roof of the abbey."

"Will they last a thousand years?" I asked. We were walking up his field towards the road.

"Aye," he said quietly. "I said if they didn'a they could bring them back."

Outside the field, at the edge of the broken road, was a small shed, like a gardener's tool shed, with a telegraph pole shooting up from its side, and the invitation 'You May Telephone From Here' on its wooden door. On the exterior wall was a clutch of three alarm bells, like a pawnbroker's sign. When anyone wants to telephone the island they call the little shed and the bell's ringing can be heard a quarter of a mile away in a force nine gale. The trouble, as John pointed out, is that his brother-in-law Donald lives nearest, so he's the one who always has to answer the phone.

*   *   *

Island roads are island roads wherever you go. They generally go uncompromisingly from one end to the other, over hills and down dips, wide enough to take one vehicle or a wandering cow, and next year they're always going to be repaired.

Because of the simplicity of the communications system it's very difficult to get lost on a small island. I got lost on Luing.

There was a cottage after a mile or so of sauntering road. No one is there now. The trees move like lost things in the garden and the falling fence encloses only old weeds and flowers brown with death. A family called Stewart lived there once, real island people. Their house was called 'Tigh-na-Mara', the house by the sea, for it faced the silver Firth of Lorn, the infant isles and the broad-backed mountains beyond. There was an old lady, Polly Stewart, and the people remember her walking out to the most difficult rocks in the teeth of a winter wind, sit fishing, and come back with a creel-full.

The sons grew and went away, and she lived alone in the island house, watched the shy northern springs become summers, and looked out on red midnights as the sun went over the hill behind her house. Then autumn, the rememberer of the year, and the winter of wild solitude. She loved them all and watched them from her house.

Tommy Ross, who has the taxi at Oban, told me the rest. "She was getting very old," he said, "and she went down to England to live. Then her son in Australia wanted her to go out there for the rest of her days. She said she would, but last summer she came back to Luing for another look.

"It was strange and marvellous to see her. Every day I used to bring her down from Oban where she stayed. Every day she crossed at Cuan Ferry and went to the old house, looking through the windows, and picking odd bits of weeds out of the garden, as though that made any difference. Old as she was she used to climb up the wee hill behind the house and sit herself down and look out across the loch. She sat for hours like that, hardly moving, every day for two weeks.

"When I drove her back at night she used to tell me all about the days on the island and we'd laugh at some of the tales. But on the last day she came down from the little hill looking very old and tired, and I took her back to Oban and she didn't speak all the way."

Standing by the frail fence I could understand, a little anyway, how old Polly Stewart felt. I turned and faced the great quiet Lorn and the huge silence of the mountains beyond. There were some shuffling cattle in the fields below but nothing else moving; no boats, no men.

I walked up the path of Polly's cottage and guiltily crouched and peeped into the kitchen window. It had curtains and a table with some crockery, a yellow packet of salt, and a pair of spectacles. I moved to the other window. Curtains again, tables and chairs, and what looked like a fox fur draped over the table. It will wait like that, I thought, for years. Until the house falls.

It needed some comedy to shift me from my mood. I provided it for myself. Seeing the furniture placed so, and the fur on the table, and some newspapers, it abruptly came to me that this might *not* be Polly Stewart's cottage after all. It might be occupied *now*. After all there were curtains at the windows. I drew back thinking anyone inside might get a shock to see a stranger pressed against the pane. Somehow I had convinced myself that I *had* made a mistake. Someone *must* live there. I moved forward a couple of inches and peered again.

There, in the window, was a face looking back at me! I jumped clear of the ground and stumbled back two paces.

It was such a shock in that overgrown place, with the wind in the trees and the chimneys, that I felt my hair lift at the nape of my neck. I stood, shaken, and then stepped forward and had another look. It was all right. It was me. Just my reflection in the dusty pane.

"Boy, am I glad to see you," I said.

Then came the point where I got lost. At the side of the cottage was a muddy path going up into a rumple of small hills. It was not anything like as substantial as the road, narrow though that was, but it had tyre marks running up it, so I concluded that the village must be in that direction. This must be the right fork that Donald had talked about.

From the start I had my suspicions. Surely no settlement, however small, and the village of Cullipool is small, could have a road so primitive leading to it. The tyre marks were those of a tractor. For much of the way they were like parallel canals, full of slate-coloured water. Between them the ground was a morass, puddings of mud and squelchy pools. Outside the bounds of the path the ground was yielding and soggy. The sheep grazed well clear of it, on the firmer, elevated ground.

I realised I would never make progress up there, scrambling along the steep sides of the minor hills, moving from one nub of rock to the next. I had to keep to the path. Sometimes it climbed among the lower hills and the water ran down it like a chute, sometimes it flattened into an honest-to-goodness bog, and at others it tipped dramatically so that the slimy water fell the opposite way.

With the over-optimistic logic of the explorer I pressed on, even though the sheep obviously thought I was out of my mind. I promised myself that if I gained the next rise I would be able to see freely to the bounding sea and Cullipool sitting at its feet. But, as always, beyond the rise was just another rise. I walked and wandered. My shoes, which had served me well through the other islands of the summer, were on the point of dying on my feet. The mud squeezed over their tops and the water seeped through their seams. My socks felt cold and horrible.

After a long time I found myself in a hollow with nothing but swamp all around me. Until then there had been the scattered islands of firm ground for which I could aim and jump, but now there was nothing. Just uncompromising ooze all around.

I cursed quite a lot during the next few minutes. It was wasted on a few unimpressed ewes and some crows, for I was alone in that windy bog, in the centre of that small cut-off land out in the November sea. I tried retracing my steps and then clinging and crawling along the earth and rock which formed the deep sides of the saucer. There was some barbed-wire up there, on a ridge, so I knew I must be near civilisation. Where there's barbed-wire, there is man.

I crawled under the bottom strand, drawing my nose and chin slowly through the greyest and smelliest of the mud, emerging on the other side with a minstrel face. Still on my hands and knees I looked up and with joy took in the beautiful arm of water rushing between Luing and Seil. Across the estuary I could see white houses and jumpy boats. Down below me, a long way down, for my muddy climb must have been a steep one, was the Luing jetty with Donald's cottage and Donald himself stumping down to the ferry boat moored at its midriff. Good. I was almost back to my starting place again.

Three paces across the now-firm grass and I knew why the barbed-wire had been there. Two feet ahead was a dramatic drop of rock and rubble — straight into a reedy bog.

Back again, under the wire, emerging with another layer of mud smeared across my face. That bottom strand was very near the ground. The Luing sheep must be fine crawlers for it to be fixed that low.

Into the bog again. Every avenue attempted was wetter and deeper than the last. Once I almost walked into one of the old slate quarry workings filled with petrified water. Then I reached the inevitable moment when I stepped out courageously hoping to find a firm place, and left my shoe behind, stuck in the last pancake of mud. My leg swung out, stockinged foot waggling before it, and, unable to stop, I placed it firmly in a particularly thick, cold, muddy mess.

I shouted swear words. The safe, stupid, self-satisfied sheep looked up with pained expressions, like bishops, from their secure hillside grazing, and the shocked crows flew hurriedly away. I pulled the foot from the mud. It came out with a gurgly sucking sound. It hung out in front of me, horribly slimy, and some wind blew about it making it feel wetter, colder, lonelier. Sobbing with the exasperation of the situation (I can endure anything but discomfort), I balanced like a stork on my other leg, gradually sinking deeper with the increased weight, and twisted gracelessly until I could get hold of my lost shoe fixed in the mud behind me.

With breathless difficulty I reached it, just got it fixed between outstretched finger and thumb, and was about to tug it out, when my knee gave way and I sat heavily in the bog. It was terrible sitting there, the water and the mud wriggling into my trousers. I made nameless moaning sounds, like the wind. Only the sheep and the crows watched.

Like a man of treacle I rose up. It mattered nothing now which way I went. I went plunging through the bog, through the reeds and the ambushing pools, like a raiding marsh arab. I fell twice, but it made no difference. The mud and the water were in my hair, in my eyes and in my underpants. Like a man feeling the raging relief of madness I charged on, through the bog, to the gradually firmer places. I terrified a family of field-mice sitting innocently among some tufts, scattering them, men, women and children, giving them something to talk about for the rest of the long winter.

Eventually this demented thing from the mire reached the little coastal road. I could see Donald's cottage and the jetty from there. I calmed myself, rather pathetically tried to brush myself down, and limped wetly towards the jetty.

Donald was on the other side with the ferry-boat. There was a klaxon on the Luing side for attracting attention, so I took some of my spite out on that, whirring the handle and sending the awful screech across the quiet water. I did it half a dozen times before I felt any better. Over on Seil, they told me afterwards, they thought there had been a major shipwreck.

He came across in the ferry, in his own steady time, tied it up and waited for me to walk down. The mud was caked all over me, I was wet and stiff with cold. I was carrying one shoe because it had given up all life, all strength and couldn't even stay on my foot. I felt unhappy and ashamed, and regretful of my treatment of Donald's klaxon.

As I walked towards the boat a dribble of muddy water issued from my trousers and trailed behind me. Donald's expression did not alter. With true Highland aplomb he looked me over and then helped me, like some war casualty, into the boat.

He backed it out and turned it into the quickly running strait. I sat miserably, feeling the wind nipping. Donald looked immediately ahead over the wheel. Nothing was said until we were half-way across. The silence was awful.

He broke it. He sniffed at the wind, and then, without turning, commented mildly: "Ye lost ye way today then?"

*　　*　　*

I went back the following morning. Donald gravely took me across on the ferry. He said nothing about my messy adventure the previous day. But as I jumped to the jetty below his house he said: "Cullipool, ye ken, is the first wee *road* on the right."

So I kept to the stony road. It was a fair day with the wind brisk and big cold clouds moving over the fawn hills of Luing. John Brown was still scything the field, his face bitter red in the wind. He saw me and called up politely: "Cullipool—the first wee *road* on your right."

The word seemed to have got around. That day, when I met an islander on the road, they pointed out the wee road on the right without even being asked. When I reached Polly Stewart's old cottage a party of sheep stood on the rising ground behind the roof and watched me tensely as though wondering if I were going to get on the wrong track again today. I disappointed them by striding purposefully on.

Luing cattle, ridiculously fat and beautiful, munched near the road and regarded me with slant eyes like Sioux in ambush.

The dimpled hills suddenly fell into a flat valley, with small feathery trees, an enclosed place, out of the wind and laden of silence. Then a solitary bird piped up somewhere on the little plain, throwing his song into the cold air. John Brown had told me to watch for this place. "The clans had a battle there once, so they say," he said. "They call it now Achafolle, the Field of Blood."

The signpost, however, pointed three ways, and said Cuan Ferry, which is where I had landed, Cullipool, which, as widely prophesied, was to the right, and Toberonochy, which was straight down the road, at the distant nose of Luing.

Being always guided by instinct rather than sense, I did not take the wee road to the right to Cullipool, nor did I walk on to Toberonochy. Instead, with some misgiving, I once more climbed from the road up a muddy track, this time to the left. It was about the same width and the same contortion as the one the day before. The mud was about the same consistency.

But this time it was the right thing to do. At the highest point of its rise I turned and, to the west, through a shallow gap in the hills, I saw a stretch of the wildest blue sea, bitten into short pieces by the wind. It swept and leaped between Luing and the Isle of Belnahua, flying white as soapsuds over skerries and around a lighthouse beleaguered on a cap of rocks. It was a seascape to make the heart leap, to excite the eyes; a bright blue and white violence that only those who live in the wild places know.

I eventually turned from it and at once, with my movement, a great hawk rose from a few feet away, lifting itself into the sky with slow flaps of wide wings. I jumped as it took off, and then stared as it went high over the upland boulders and hung in the vacant sky. Walking on, still watching it, I turned a corner and came into a sheltered vale. The road sloped quickly now and wound into a kernel of the island where there was a farmhouse and some other comforting building. I could hear chickens arguing and water tumbled over an old millstone. Bare trees, white barked, fanned out behind the settlement. You could see the sea through the branches and they retained last summer's rookery.

There was a woman with greying hair, wearing a thick jumper, trousers and boots, feeding the hens. Uncertainly I called 'Good afternoon' and she looked up and laughed.

"Ah," she said. "You took the left fork instead o' the right, then." No longer surprised at the island bush-telegraph, I agreed that this was the case.

Her name was Irene Maclachlan. She had been born in that farmhouse fifty-seven years before, and she had never married. Her parents worked the farm by the sea until they died. Her forbears had been on Luing in the sixteenth century.

"I'm alone here," she said. "But I wouldn't have it any other way. I've always lived in this house and I can't see me going away now."

She led the way into the crouching house with her family's hunting tartan on the thick wooden door. "Lonely?" she smiled when I asked. "Too much to do. And at night I get the tilly lamp burning in here, and bolt the door. With a good fire and a good book, or listening to the wireless, I'm quite content. The storms can bang at the windows as much as they like."

It was a close room with the cooking stove next to the dresser, some wooden chairs and a table, and a chest where Irene Maclachlan kept her store of books. Her precious radio set is covered up each day until the evening sets in. It sits just under a framed portrait of Reginald Forte, the BBC organist, which he signed and sent to her in 1936.

"I only have the chickens around the farm now," she said. "I don't even have a dog. Every day I row the wee boat out there to Torsa to feed the cattle." She pointed from the window to a flat island lying half a mile offshore in the Lorn waters. "They belong to the Luing herd and they take them across at the low autumn tide and leave them there for the winter. I have to go over to give them the cattle feed that's stored there. It's quite a journey there and back on a winter's morning, but I'm accustomed to it."

Then she said she couldn't swim, but it didn't worry her because this was the lee side of the island and the sea never got very rough.

We went out into the garden again. It was sheltered there, in the dell, and the trees were touched silver with the pale sun. "The earth in the garden," Irene Maclachlan said, "is all Irish. It was brought over here at the time of the great potato famine in Ireland. We had potatoes here and the little Irish vessels used to come up and get them and they used the earth as ballast. When they threw it out the people here at that time used it for the garden. I'm always expecting to see a shamrock sprouting."

We walked up the muddy path, the way I had come. She showed me the sheading, the cattle shed of the old farm, now in ruins, and the remains of the mill and the miller's house.

"There's a fort up on the hill," she said pointing. "Just a pile of stones now. It's very ancient, nobody seems to know just how much. There's another on the next hill. They could signal to each other and there are others stretched out along the mainland connected with these two." We walked by a staunch wall of loaf-sized stones. "My grandfather built this wall from stones he took from the fort. Then somebody told him he was destroying an ancient monument and he ought to put the stones back. Well he didn't take any more, but he didn't put them back either. It's a fine wall, isn't it?"

*   *   *

Cullipool, to the right down the wee road, is a salty village, facing the winds and the seas that fly across from the Isle of Mull. On this day of bitter wind I looked from the black-slated shore of Luing across the charging waves to the dramatic mountains of Mull. It was a remote, wild, thrilling sight, standing on that naked shore. A dog loped from one of the Cullipool houses, but I saw no people at all. Lobster fishers had left their pots and their small boats on the land above the sea, but the men had gone.

From there I could look over the violent channel to the beleaguered lighthouse and the suddenly rising body of Belnahua. One gale of a night in the autumn of 1936 a small ship, a Latvian cargo vessel called the *Helena Faulraums*, dipping and shuddering through the terrifying Hebridean seas, ran into the toothy rocks of Belnahua.

It is still talked about by the Luing islanders. "A terriba night, terriba," said Archie MacLea who lives in the village and works the ferry with Donald. "I was a boy at school, I remember, and early in the morning my pal came over to the house and called to me, 'Archie, see all the driftwood on the beach'. We ran down to the beach and all the wood was floating about. We didn'a realise anything about the ship, ye ken. We thought it was just wood. Then we saw a piece of the deckhouse and the wheel, and we knew what had happened.

"Some o' the village men came and they went into the water and they found a body floating face down, and then another and they brought them ashore. I remember them carrying them up."

There's a tumbled old church isolated in the middle of Luing and the men who died that furious night are buried there. One, the radio officer who was on his first voyage, lies in a single grave with his photograph under glass on the headstone. It is a strange and sad sight. He was a young, handsome man and the photograph, sealed in its globular frame, has not faded or discoloured in thirty and more years. His parents in Latvia had the headstone sent from their own country and the epitaph is in crude, poignant poetry, composed by someone in that far country who knew a little English, but not much. It says:

> Radiote Legrath Albert Sultcs.
> Died Oct. 26th 1936
> Was storm — Tore blossoms.
> Destroyed dreams of
> Happyness.

A few steps away, by the wall of the churchyard, is another grave with an encyclopaedic tombstone that has so much to say that it runs its entire length, runs up the wall and falls down the other side to the road. The man who lies there, Alex Campbell, dug his own grave and prepared his own stone. He was a bit premature because he lived nine years after he did the digging and he had to keep returning to the churchyard to bale out any water and shovel up any earth which had fallen into it. Over those years he kept thinking up things to say on his headstone so that it got longer and longer as he lived on.

On the exterior of the churchyard wall the stone demands 'Halt Passengers and Take Heed'. The words roll on from there. A warning that mockers and knockers of his epitaph should remember the "judgement on the children who cried 'bald-head' (II Kings ii. 23)". Since, if you recall that rather unpleasant story, the forty-two infants who called after Elisha "Go up thou bald head" were promptly eaten by two she-bears, similar judgement seems rather unlikely in the middle of an island in the Hebrides.

The late Mr. Campbell goes on to quote the Psalms with "It is a marvellous headstone in the eyes of the builders" and chipped out on two separate occasions is the revelation that he dug his own grave as Jacob did, and a warning that nobody else must be buried with him. Bits of poetry and philosophy are all over the place. If it's not too cold he provides a marvellous afternoon's reading.

It was late when I got to Toberonochy, the white village at the far end of Luing. Quiet and late, the small houses facing the single rough street. The sun, finishing his short stint was sliding behind the high back of Jura. The Lorn water was touched with a cold brightness. All the mountains on the mainland shore were growing dim, except for one, distant but startling in the last sun. It was high and far away. But the eye went to it at once. It was covered with the first snow. The winter was near. My journey to the islands was almost accomplished.

Snow and a Seal

If now I remember St. Agnes in the Scillies as my isle of the spring, think of Caldy and its fuchsias of a hot June, and Herm in the brown of autumn, then Lindisfarne is my winter island.

The wind shouted and the snow lay in sheets and pillows over the sand flats of this most extraordinary of places. There were young seals among the rocks, looking like snow themselves, swans clustered like deep drifts. The sky and the sea were black with cold, except when a huge winter sunset bled along the whole of Northumberland. And I saw a heron in lovely slow flight across the bitter landscape.

I had hesitated to go there because Lindisfarne, Holy Isle, is not an island as the others are. When the tide has gone it is seen to be stitched to the mainland by a great hem of sand set with pools of jewelled water, strutted by birds and inhabited by sharp winds and salty creatures. In distant history it was described as twice an island, twice a continent in one day. This oddity generates its own island lore. A party of policemen once went to Holy Isle to catch one of the pubs open after hours. The tide came in while they were there and they could not get back to the mainland. Every islander apologised but his house was full and he had no room to put them up. Nor were there any boats available. There was no food and no drink (for the pub was, of course, closed) and the unhappy officers walked the night in that dark and chilly place before they could escape across the sands at morning.

Now there is a causeway like a leg that juts out from the Northumberland shore, across the flats and banks which they call the Slakes, and reaches Holy Isle at its middle. At high tide it is still impossible to get across and there are refuge boxes on stilts for the traveller who gets caught, as many have been, by the home-going flow.

But for all this connection to the mainland this special place is as much an island as any I have walked. It has that quality of remoteness, the feeling of being beleaguered by God in a far sea, a rocky independence, and a lasting quietness, and these are the treasures of such places. Its people live, for the most part, content with their isolation, only looking upon the slender causeway as a means of strangers coming and going; it is as though they themselves feel they have no right of way across it. Simply because they are islanders and this is their island. On the road north, not far short of the Scottish border you first see the isle riding the waves, out by itself with the flat backs of the Farnes islands further south, so that Holy Isle is like the vanguard of a fleet. From the plump, satisfying farming country of Northumberland they are a prospect of wildness, of distant, fierce romance; adventurers, pirates off the coast. Their bows are in the waves, and even those miles away you can see the stripes of foam lighting the inky sea. At night the Longstone lighthouse signals its stint and you feel that, in profile gauge to the corner where the chamfer meets the surface of the hole G″ diameter. This method of measuring is quite suitable for the roughing operations, but for finishing to limits of 0·00025 in. it is far from satisfactory.

It would, of course, be quite satisfactory to remove the strip and take reliable measurements, or length comparisons by means of precision gauge blocks used in conjunction with a suitable optical microscope. In toolrooms not possessing these instruments, improvised methods have to be developed by toolmakers. The following were employed in making a gauge similar to that shown in Fig. 138. Each dimension was measured by special measuring mediums in the form of precision gauges, being designed and made in a manner that ensured sufficient accuracy for the particular dimension for which each was intended—as in this case being for the purpose of measuring a gauge, they are master gauges. These master gauges have, of course, to be made before commencing to machine the workpiece, and this necessitates carefully planning beforehand the methods and mediums to be applied where any difficulty in measuring will be encountered.

When making one or only a few cylindrical profile gauges the master gauges can be made from mild steel; when they are to be used continuously, however, to preserve their accuracy, the master gauges should be made from a tool or die steel carefully hardened and ground where possible. It is assumed in this description of machining the form of the cylindrical profile gauge that the master gauges have been made. They are six in number, and details of their dimensions and shape are given in Fig. 140. At the end of the description of making the profile gauge, details of measuring methods used for making the master gauges are given, also methods for setting to close angular limits of accuracy the lathe swivel slide for turning short-tapered work and similar methods for turning long-tapered work.

The order of operations in machining the profile gauge form is set to suit the particular master gauges employed and must of necessity be adhered to, but where the application of the master gauges is not affected by the order of operations, however, it can be changed to the turner's liking, the best policy probably then being to machine the most difficult parts first, as error being more likely to develop there is not so much previous machining to repeat when facing back the form of the gauge profile for correction.

x"=1½. Length of hole 1"dia.

A"+B"+C"+D"+1"

Fine knurled finish

1"-0001"

GO ·1874·5" NOT GO ·1875·0"

1" to -·015"

1/32 rad.   1/32"chamfer at 45°
1"-0001"

NO.1 THIS SINGLE END PROGRESSIVE TYPE OF PLUG GAUGE IS VERY SUITED
FOR MEASURING HOLES SITUATED DEEPLY IN THE WORKPIECE, AS THE
"GO"MEMBER ALINES THE GAUGE FOR TRYING THE "NOT GO"MEMBER.

G"-   GO   NOT GO   G"+.

Rad   Chamfer at 45°
NO.2 DOUBLE ENDED STANDARD TYPE PLUG GAUGE FOR HOLE G"DIAMETER.

C'   A"+B" ±·0001"
x"= G"-1/16 to 1/4"

Crest of cone
removed
leaving 1/32"
wide flat
acme.   2β°

Tap 1/4" B.S.F.
3/8" deep

G"- for
push fit

1/8"   Clearance recess

NO.3 GAUGE FOR DEPTH OF PARALLEL HOLE G"DIAMETER & CHAMFER β°.

D"-(K"+1/16")
-θ°

Tap 3/16 B.S.F. 1/4" deep,
recess front 7/32"dia.
1/16" deep

H"±0001"

NO.4 GAUGE FOR TAPER θ° DIAMETER OF LARGE END H"& DISTANCE OF
DIAMETER H"FROM FRONT DATUM FACE OF THE CYLINDRICAL PROFILE
GAUGE

Undercut in corner of shoulder
A"+B"+C"+D" ±·0001"   Tap 1/4" B.S.F. 3/8" deep

1"dia.-for
push fit

1"dia·0025"
·003"   1/32"
rad.

G"-
Push
fit

3/6"

1/8(A+B)   Clearance recess

NO.5 GAUGE FOR MEASURING THE DISTANCE FROM THE FRONT DATUM FACE OF
THE C.P. GAUGE TO WHERE THE RADIUS K"MEETS THE SURFACE OF THE HOLE 1"DIA

Clearance recess
F"dia ±0001"

B"

2α°

G"dia push
fit

1/32 rad.   G"-1/32" 1/16"   Tap 1/4" B.S.F. 3/8" deep

NO.6 GAUGE FOR MEASURING THE DIAMETER DEPTH & ANGLE OF THE CHAMFER α°

Fig. 140.—Showing master gauges Nos. 1 to 6.

those outlands, outlandish things occur, that the home-safe mainlander can never know.

At Beal a lane leaves the major road and runs down to the wide, coloured estuary, and to Holy Isle. As with all islands the first full sight is an adventure. I stopped and took it in and knew I had made the right journey. It lay over there, the tide growing around it, so that, on that day, it was founded on sand and sea and snow.

It was low, cautiously hilly at its lower lip, with the indistinct pile of its castle and village at the rising point.

It was the approach that was unique, the journey that the pilgrims trod, for this was the most venerable place in all of England in the early times of Christianity. There was a breathless winter beauty about it. The wind from the north cutting up the flat pools and the running water of the deeper channel. The cakes of snow lying on the acres of sand; strange companions, one the silent child of winter, one the playmate of shouting summer and the long warm days. And the birds! What marvellous birds were stalking the flats, swans and gulls and greylag geese, probing sandpipers, and fat mallard; the tern, the kittiwake, and the St. Cuthbert duck, the December citizens of this cold and lovely channel. Then I saw the heron flying, and that was something I had never seen. Whenever I have come upon one in these island travels it has been standing, frowning, and now I saw it fly in the same manner, slow, thoughtful, preoccupied, a lot on its mind.

On the island side of the Slakes there were, at first, high dunes, thick with marran grass with the wind flowing through it as it might run through the long soft hair of a girl.

Then the land curved with the channel and then I caught sight of the frontiers of the sea, curling violent breakers, indistinct in their own spray, falling like wild drunks over the sand bar, moving in to encircle the entire island at the appointed time as indicated in the Tables of Time and Tides.

Far out, just low lines in the sea, I could see the Farnes group, unoccupied now except for the seals and the birds, and the men at the Longstone light.

There was some snow lying about in the streets of the village, but it was patchy and scattered with nothing of the depth of the mainland fall. There was no movement in the streets, no sound except the wind taking the corners. At the end of one row of stone houses was a pub called the Iron Rails. There was the warm reflection of a fire in its windows. I went in.

A young man in a speckled grey and black jersey, with sea-waders like stilts thrust out before him, stretched out beside the fire. His fair hair stuck straight out from his head and he smiled with a broken tooth. He was a lobster fisherman called Jimmy Brigham. Everyone called him Clinker and I knew immediately I looked at him that here was an island character.

*   *   *

They called him Clinker, he said, because at the island school he used to wear heavy-studded boots and as he scraped along they used to sound 'Clinker, Clanker'. The name grew up with him.

"Mind," he said as we walked the broken beach in the jagged wind, "everybody here's got a nickname. George Moody, him behind the bar in the Iron Rails, they call him 'Bash'. I don't know why and I don't think he does. We've got a man called 'Dancer' and a few others with some funny names, I can tell you."

His voice was the Northumberland tone, but overlaid with something richer, thicker, something perhaps left by the Danes or other people from the sea. He took me to the hill on which the castle squats, overlooking, in the best tradition of the drama, the great waves of the northern ocean. The wind was so fierce up there that we could only walk by bending our bodies into it like hunchbacks, and keeping our faces low out of the sting of the bits of snow and ice that flew across the land.

There were three herring drifters, turned over on their fat stomachs years ago and cut in half to make storage sheds on the headland. I had seen them used like that in the Orkneys and Shetlands, and in other island places. What a strange task it must have been cutting through a stout boat like that. Something like sawing a fat woman in half. Clinker and I got around the leeward side of them.

"Used to be a lot of fishing off here years ago," he shouted. We were out of the feel of the wind but not out of its bawling. "Dead now. See the boats in the harbour. The third one is mine."

I looked across the spine of hill. The Lindisfarne harbour was ruffled and metallic in a stray moment of winter sun. The quartet of small boats rode musically. Behind them was a sturdy mole jutting out protectively and then the dark-sheeted estuary with the shivering hills of the mainland white against the heavy sky. To the right of the boats, beyond the little harbour, the skeleton of Lindisfarne Priory stood, columns and arches, thin as a copse of naked trees.

Out to sea a rash of duck sped just above the waves. Clinker, who by reputation is rarely without a gun, eyed them speculatively. The breaking of the seas on the first limbs of the Holy Isle sands was big and angry, as though they were surprised and hurt to find such opposition so far from the mainland shore for which they were heading. They fell and floundered, the black waves turning cream, the sea-birds crying in their everlasting excitement as though such a thing had never before happened.

"Never get out there on a day like this," said Clinker. "Once it was seven weeks before we could get the boat from the harbour. The lobsters must have thought we'd given up altogether. There's one boat trying white fishing around these parts now. Everybody's waiting to see how they get on."

He pointed beyond the sea. "Inner Farne, Longstone, Brownsman and the other islands," he said. "How far?" I asked.

"Five miles," he said. "But the farthest places in the world on a day like this. We even had our own lifeboatmen marooned out there once."

I said: "Longstone was Grace Darling's lighthouse, wasn't it?" "Aye. She was a Bamburgh girl," he said as though he knew her. "We've got that picture of her in the bar of the Iron Rails."

Turning away from the churning sea I looked out from behind our upturned herring drifter over the back of the island. It was like being an observer in a front-line trench. From the high point where we stood the land rolled quickly away to a plain of pastures and animals, and then further still the sand banks once more and the shallows of the north-eastern channel. It was a wide landscape to see all at once, grey and green, dotted with sheep and cows, with no buildings in view. Down below us, going towards the extreme flat tongue of land, against the hard wind a woman was walking a dog along the fringe of the sea. She walked, as we had walked, bent against the force but making good progress, and the dog jumped in the gusts and tried to catch swooping gulls.

Clinker and I then went down from the knoll to the other side of the harbour to find a lifeboatman called Henderson who breeds pigeons, but he was not around his boathouse, and anyway, as we went along the lip of the beach we saw a baby seal lying among the rocks and bladderwrack below.

"Grey seal," said Clinker briefly. We went down over the inky rocks, across the broken sand and the toothy outcrops, to the place where the seal was lying. He looked up with interest as we got near as though he had been having a nap.

His great pool eyes gazed at us as though we were some old friends he had been waiting to see. He was about four feet long. His whiskers were dainty and his face very tender.

"Keep away from his head," warned Clinker. "One bite and he'll have your foot off." He got behind the seal and it turned and snarled at him like a mastiff. It snapped determinedly, but its turn was clumsy and gave him plenty of time to get clear. It barked gruffly like an elderly dog.

"Came in with the tide," said Clinker crouching and examining it like a doctor with an irritable patient. "It wasn't here this morning, though there were some white ones further up the beach."

"Can we get it back into the water?" I suggested.

Without answering, Clinker gently cuffed the seal on the rump and it started to hobble and jerk towards the verge of the sea where the current swirled about a small archipelago of rock and sand islands. One cuff, one hop, that's how it went, with the seal looking back over its shoulder in annoyance and barking throatily with each jump nearer the sea. Eventually its flippers found the water and it slid through the cold shallows before reaching a safe depth and turning to look at us. If ever an animal poked out its tongue at a human that one did. Then it turned and swam off with the current. I was full of gladness that we had seen the seal and glad too that it was away in the sea. We climbed the banks from the sand to the grass again. We turned and we could just see its whitish head pushing through the small inshore waves.

Then Clinker said: "Lot of good that will do it. It'll never find its mother now and it's too young to fish. It'll be dead in a week."

*   *   *

They called the pub the Iron Rails, so George Moody thinks anyway, because there was a quarry on the island once and there was a single-track railway for getting the stone away. It ended just outside the door of the bar.

George, a young man with a round face and a mat of black hair, has given the picture of Grace Darling the pride of the mantle-shelf, above the wide fire. She rows, with set, cherubic Victorian expression, through the storm on the way to her famous rescue of the crew of the *Forfarshire*, their ship impaled on the vicious Harcar Rocks. That was in the autumn of 1838. "Bamburgh girl," nodded George as though he knew her too.

On the shelf above the fire is a coiled viper, its neck broken in the right spot, shells and bottles and odd bits picked up from the sea and shore, and brought into the pub for good keeping. George has behind his bar bottles of Lindisfarne mead which is today made just up the road in the village. It's amber and has a gentle sweetness. It appears an innocuous drink until you've had a few glasses. I wondered how the monks of old kept sober.

There were a few others in the bar, Captain Roberts, the lifeboat secretary, Clinker, Hector Douglas, the second mechanic of the lifeboat, and a tall man with a narrow brown face and glasses who had an island accent so thick I could not understand one word in twenty. The others called him Chichester and he looked remarkably like the round-the-world mariner. But I don't think he was all that pleased at the nickname.

We talked of island birds, for these men, like all those who live in the outlandish places, knew the names of all the creatures of the sky, watch them come and go, and can foretell the weather of approaching seasons from the times and the journeys, and how long the migrants stay. The chubby eider duck they call the St. Cuthbert duck, although this has become 'Culba-duck' in the local language. The Arctic akua is called the shitty-go-alan, although they don't tell people this until they get to know them reasonably well.

At this north-sea landfall, a grateful place for birds on their great travels, the famous Eagle Clarke, the pioneer of the study of bird migration in Britain, watched, walked and waited through many a long autumn. Today these powerful fishermen who get their living on the windy coasts will tell you without embarrassment how they have picked up tiny birds with their hands, birds too tired to fly another inch, and brought them to safe places on the islands to rest.

The talk went around to disasters and rescues off the isle. Like most islanders they have the skeleton of the wreckers in their cupboards. Up here, not many generations ago, the people were said to see a ship driven before a storm and to go out on the rocks and pray: "Lord God, send her to us. Send her to us."

They have more than made up for it since. Hector Douglas, a small, domesticated-looking man, has been out with the lifeboat on many a screaming night, taken from a soft bed to the cold soul-less sea. He was one of the men marooned a few winters ago on desolate Inner Farne.

"There was us and the Seahouses boat," he remembered. "We'd been out to a trawler, but the sea got so terrible on the way back that we couldn't get home, so we tried to shelter on the lee of Inner Farne. It was still bad there, very bad and we couldn't get the boats near the shore because we would have smashed them. And we was taking such a hiding that we couldn't stay in the boats either.

"They sent one of them helicopters out after us. Brave fellas they were, going out in that weather. And me, who'd never had my feet a foot above the ground before, except in bed, found myself being hoisted up on this cable and swung out over the waves and dropped on Inner Farne. Just like that. Strange feeling. When they'd got everybody ashore they went off and left us there. The storm was too heavy for them to stay in that contraption."

He drank and grinned. "Sixteen of us from the two

lifeboats and the fellas from the fishing boat too on the island. Three days stuck there, we were, and the storm never let up. The boats were bouncing at their anchors offshore, but we were not much more comfortable. The wind and the cold rain and nothing to eat but a bit of hard tack, and it *was* hard tack, and one rabbit. The second mechanic of the Seahouses boat caught that. But there wasn't much to go round between us."

George Moody said: "They've got a store of food and blankets on Inner Farne now."

"Aye," agreed Hector, nodding over his beer. "It's all locked up over there, so you have to have a key to get at it if you're ever marooned." He sniffed. "And," he added, "we've got the key."

*   *   *

Just up-channel from the place where Clinker and I found the grey seal, a few hundred yards offshore is a black, flat islet, a mere finger of rock and a few tufts of hard grass. Standing on this, on this day, starkly against the background of the high snow on the mainland, is a sturdy cross.

December dark was overtaking the afternoon when first I saw it. The sea in the channel was moving and cold, but away from the big breakers on the sandbar. A few silhouetted birds crossed the dusk. The cross is so stark, so brave and blatant, and yet so poignant that it compels you to stand and look at it for a long time. It is as though you expected something to move or to happen. Nothing does. The place is called St. Cuthbert's Isle; the place where Cuthbert, a farm boy from the hills of Lammermuir, found peace and God.

I surprised myself by staggering off across heads of rock and great growths of seaweed, trying to pick a way through the icy pools increasing every moment with the tide. I wanted to get closer; to see it better. It was just two hundred yards away when I had to stop or drown. There seemed to be nothing in that corner of shore, nothing but water, patched snow, black rock, and that great upstanding cross.

The vicar of Holy Island, Denis Bill, can see it from the window of his house. In his cheerful living-room his sons, John, aged eight, and David, eighteen months and known as 'Tonto', played before the fire with racing cars. They revved them spectacularly. St. Cuthbert's little isle was set like a sad picture in the window frame. The Reverend Bill is a pipe-smoking vicar with silver hair and a bland nature. He and his young wife laugh over her name, which is Minnie. "Minnie Bill," he grinned, "sounds like the name of a fishing boat!" She is the island's nurse. They love the place because of its friendly quietness, the closeness of the sea, the sound of the wind around their roof at night, and the special feeling of being in a place where the brave early saints worked and walked. If ever he feels disheartened he has only to look from his window at that cross on the dark islet.

He has a great feeling for the people too. "Not long ago," he said, "it was the women who launched the lifeboat. They'd come from their houses on the most dreadful nights. There are people on Holy Isle who saw their mothers go out every dawn with baskets of fish fixed on the panniers of little donkeys, off to the mainland towns to sell them.

"In the old days the islanders had horses and carts, and every horse knew the safe way across the sands even when the tide was coming in. The first bus ever seen here came over the Slakes with its windows all blacked out to pick up two German airmen who crashed their plane on the seashore during the war."

He smiled and looked across to the small isle where St. Cuthbert's cross was now caught up with the early darkness. "Islanders here from the saints onward have always been resourceful," he said. "At the beginning of the war the military people, with that odd sort of misplaced enthusiasm that we all had in those early days, brought over a whole lot of motor cars and stuck them out on the sands with the idea of preventing the enemy landing gliders. Well one or two of the cars weren't at all bad and, as I said, islanders are ever resourceful. I heard that there was quite a passable Daimler running around here for some time after that."

He told me about the island weddings. "Just outside the church door," he said, "you will see a stone with a cavity worn into the top. Every woman who has been married on Lindisfarne since goodness-knows-when has been required to jump up on to that stone, with the two oldest men in the village holding her hands. If she can jump down without stumbling then hers will be a happy life.

"The church gate is tied with rope and the bride has to pay ten shillings to get out. Then, outside, all the other island men fire shotguns into the air. Every wedding is a shotgun affair here."

We talked then of St. Cuthbert, but the vicar confessed himself to "being something of a fan of St. Aidan" who came first to the island from Iona and began that small imperishable settlement from which Christianity spread and shone throughout all the northern kingdom of Britain.

There is a redstone statue of St. Aidan in his churchyard, a gaunt, vivid representation of a tremendous man, holding a burning torch to this world of sea and sky and wild coast. Denis Bill walked with me to his gate. It was fully dark now. There were some yellow lights, little squares like sails, in the houses along the shore. On the mainland more and busier lights twinkled. But there was no sound on the island, only the advances of the sea below and the wind above.

"I think I understand how Aidan felt in Lindisfarne," he said. "You can feel the peace of a place like this and have the knowledge of all the tremendous things that have happened here. Listen to the sea now. It's right in now, making us a real island again. That reminds me, I'm on coastguard watch tonight. I must go."

*   *   *

The venerable Priory on Holy Isle is rare among relics because it has become ruined *upwards*. No half-buried mounds, grass-covered walls nor pieces sticking out like old teeth here. The superb symmetry of the warm redstone columns is still there to be admired with one joyful rainbow arch flung across the sky like some brave gesture or glad salutation. The Norman walls themselves have mostly fallen, but the uprights remain and on this, my second day on the isle, they framed the gentle, cold scene of snow drifting across boats in harbour and the strong head of the castle topping the furthermost hill where I had stood with Clinker against the old herring boats.

From this place, although nothing of their earlier abbey remains, came the beautifully *human* Lindisfarne Gospels. They were written by the monks at the beginning of the eighth century and to them this delightful footnote was added:

> *Eadfrith, Bishop of the Church of Lindisfarne, he at first wrote this book for God and St. Cuthbert, and for all the saints in common that are in the island and Ethilwald, Bishop of those of Lindisfarne Island bound and covered it outwardly as well as he could. And Billfrith, the anchorite, he wrought as a smith the ornaments that are on the outside, and adorned it with gold and with gems, also with silver overgilded, a treasure without deceit. And Alfred, an unworthy and most miserable priest, with God's help and St. Cuthbert's, overglossed it in English.*

What a picture. I could see them all there that day as I stood. The hefty Billfrith, strong as his name, sleeves up, sweating, his habit open down his chest, hammering the precious metals over his anvil; Ethilwald bookbinding conscientiously but not all that well; Alfred, runny-nosed, moaning and grumbling at every letter.

The monks, as on Skellig and their other fastnesses in the sea, were always prey to the Norse raiders who harboured no ideas about fair play and non-combatants. They were set upon at regular times through the years, and in the middle of the ninth century in the face of a Danish raid, they fled to Durham, taking with them the Gospel, the hard work of Eadfrith, Ethilwald, Billfrith and the complaining Alfred, and digging up the body of St. Cuthbert and taking that with them too. It was the most extraordinary moonlight flit in history.

* * *

I left the castle until last. Snow was coming in thinly but horizontally on the cutting wind as I went out that way, out to the extremity of the land, up the stone path that rises above the trembling sea. Coming down was Old Robert, a sort of ancient retainer at the castle, somewhere in his eighties and moving through the winter wind at a shuffle.

He carried some logs for his cottage fire in the village and a small empty milk churn. I called a greeting to him, but the gale blew my voice away. But I could hear him as he came down under his cap, in his sailor jersey and wellington boots. For he sang as he shuffled:

> Onward Christian soldiers,
> Marching as to war. . . .

Old Robert stopped. He was well disposed to talk, despite the weather. Every day for years he had walked the mile to the village and then back with the post and the milk, and then done the journey again, and perhaps a third time, moving at an infinitesimal rate. He had lively eyes set deep in an ancient face. Small splinters of white whiskers thrust themselves cheerfully out from his chin and his cheeks and as we talked, so that snowflakes caught upon them and built on them. It was the most curious sight because as we talked so his old face became gradually snowbound, the tiny drifts built up all over it, until at the finish only his bright eyes were free of it.

As he talked or snorted through his nostrils, as he did at intervals, some snow fell away, but it was soon replaced. I tried tactfully to manoeuvre around, but the flakes were swirling thinly in all directions and they seemed to be heading for Old Robert as though they knew that the deep crevices of his face would provide them with some shelter.

I asked him about a shipwreck in 1892 when all the crew but one of a vessel called the *Holmrook* perished off Lindisfarne. I had seen their collective grave in the churchyard, each man named except the last who was recorded as 'And another unidentified'.

This had fascinated me, bothered me, ever since I had read it. Who was this 'another unidentified'? Resisting the temptation to brush or blow the gathering snow from the old man's face I asked him whether he remembered the wreck. He was bright and lucid and didn't seem to notice the wind or the snow.

"Aye," he shouted above the weather. "Like it was last week. There was one who lived. We called him Sailor Jack. He had a broken leg and it was a-snowing just like today. He dragged that leg across the snow to a house and said that the ship had gone down."

I peered at him through his thickening barrier of snow. "Didn't Sailor Jack know who the other man was in the wreck—the one they didn't name?" I questioned loudly.

"No!" said Old Robert so decidedly that a minor avalanche fell from his nose and eyebrows. "Nobody never knew. He was just a dead man. Stowaway, could be, or a sailor who signed on late. Just a dead man."

He said he had to be going to get his fire burning and I was afraid to detain him in case the collecting snow should harm him, for he was very old. We said a shouted farewell and he went an inch at a time down the slope towards the harbour and the village, and still singing, *not* from the start of the verse but where he had been interrupted:

> With the Cross of Jesus
> Going on before. . . .

The castle door was up a further slope, exposed to the whole temper of that unruly day. I was high above the whole island there, above the curling black sea with the thin snow flying across it. There was a rope threaded to the side of the castle wall. I was glad of its help.

Outside the castle door I paused. I was, I realised, on the threshold of a most curious situation. The castle was not old, as castles go, merely sixteenth century restored massively in Queen Victoria's reign. But, thrust out there on that rock over the ocean, in the wild whistling of winter, it had all the ancient eeriness of any fortress. It has a private owner and it was shut to visitors for the winter, that I knew also. But inside, living in it as though it was a semi-detached in Merton and Morden, was a family, George Lilburn, the caretaker, his wife, his sister and his daughter.

At the front door a notice in iron said: 'Please ring the bell'. I had never rung a castle bell before so I looked around for it. It was fifteen feet up the solid wall and there was no rope. Cautiously I opened the heavy door. The wind screeched in. I half expected to hear an anguished shout: "Shut the door!"

Instead I found myself in a hollow passage. I pushed the door creaking shut behind me. There were some dim steps. I went up and opened another door and, surprised, walked out on to the roof of one of the towers of the castle. There were some pigeons sheltering from the wind up there. The snow seemed to have faltered and stopped. But the wind still struck against the stone parapet and fled across the battlements. Another door, and another, and then I found them.

No more curious sight had ever come my way in all my island travels. Mr. and Mrs. Lilburn, Linda Lilburn, his sister, and another Linda Lilburn, his daughter, were sitting out the winter around the castle fire, a transistor making music on the side.

This Englishman's castle was his home. "Come on in," he said. "But shut the door." I joined them at their strange fireside. They did not seem to think that there was anything obviously unusual about living in a remote stone bastion sticking out into the icy sea from a cold shoulder of England.

"Been here sixty-four years. All my life," said George Lilburn. He was spare and bald and wearing a Holy Island sweater like the other men had been. I recognised him from his portrait hanging on the wall of the saloon bar of the Northumberland Arms, the pub next door to the Iron Rails. "I used to run around this castle when I was a little lad and my father was caretaker here before me. It's warmer now because we've got the central heating in some of the rooms."

His wife, his sister and his daughter were all born on the island. The family there goes back into dim history. His daughter Linda works in the mead distillery in the village.

The castle is full of ancient furniture, candlesticks, four-poster beds, with secret compartments for guns and jewels, strange passages with slit-width windows. They lived, ate and slept in this eerie pile, with, they admitted, the noises of night and deep shadows in the day. But they would never be away from the island. The two Lindas were called so after Lindisfarne. The castle and the island were lovely in the summer when the sea was blue, they said.

"Is there anything you don't like about living here?" I asked.

Mrs. Lilburn looked up at the remote ceiling and around the walls of massive masonry.

"It gets ever so dusty," she said.

*   *   *

So I went from there, my last island, the final step of my journey. It seemed a long way back to the village in the freezing wind, but I would not have had it any other way, for I had known these little places in all the seasons, met their people and tasted their life.

I was nearly in the village, pressing on against the gathering dark and the cold. I turned to look at the black pile of the wintry castle, alone out there on its windy shelf. Then I heard someone coming towards me and the low chanting of "Onward Christian Soldiers". Old Robert shuffled, still painfully slow but cheerful, through the raw night. He had disposed of his logs, but he had the milk can in his hand. He was going back to the castle.

He laughed, a croaking sound, when he saw me. "Ho! Ho!" he gurgled. "Fergot me milk. Always fergetting something."

harlie and the Chocolate Factory

ROALD DAHL

Charlie and the Chocolate Factory

Illustrated by Quentin Blake

ALFRED A. KNOPF
New York

THIS IS A BORZOI BOOK PUBLISHED BY ALFRED A. KNOPF

www.randomhouse.com/kids

Library of Congress Cataloging-in-Publication Data
Dahl, Roald.
Charlie and the chocolate factory / by Roald Dahl ; illustrated by Quentin Blake.
p. cm.
Summary: Each of five children lucky enough to discover an entry ticket into Mr. Willy Wonka's
mysterious chocolate factory takes advantage of the situation in his own way.
[1. Humorous stories. 2. Behavior—Fiction.] I. Blake, Quentin, ill. II. Title.
PZ7.D1515 Ch 2001
[Fic]—dc21   2001029461

ISBN 0-375-81526-0 (trade)
ISBN 0-375-91526-5 (lib. bdg.)

Printed in the United States of America

September 2001

10 9 8 7 6 5 4 3 2

Revised Edition

For Theo

CONTENTS

Charlie and the Chocolate Factory

1
Here Comes Charlie

THESE TWO VERY OLD PEOPLE are the father and mother of
Mr. Bucket. Their names are Grandpa Joe and Grandma
Josephine.

And *these* two very old people are the father and mother of Mrs. Bucket. Their names are Grandpa George and Grandma Georgina.

This is Mr. Bucket.   This is Mrs. Bucket.

Mr. and Mrs. Bucket have a small boy whose name is Charlie Bucket.

This is Charlie.

How d'you do? And how d'you do? And how d'you do again?

He is pleased to meet you.

The whole of this family—the six grownups (count them) and little Charlie Bucket—live together in a small wooden house on the edge of a great town.

The house wasn't nearly large enough for so many people, and life was extremely uncomfortable for them all. There were only two rooms in the place altogether, and there was only one bed. The bed was given to the four old grandparents because they were so old and tired. They were so tired, they never got out of it.

Grandpa Joe and Grandma Josephine on this side, Grandpa George and Grandma Georgina on this side.

Mr. and Mrs. Bucket and little Charlie Bucket slept in the other room, upon mattresses on the floor.

In the summertime, this wasn't too bad, but in the winter, freezing cold drafts blew across the floor all night long, and it was awful.

There wasn't any question of them being able to buy a better house—or even one more bed to sleep in. They were far too poor for that.

Mr. Bucket was the only person in the family with a job. He worked in a toothpaste factory, where he sat all day long at a bench and screwed the little caps onto the tops of the tubes of toothpaste after the tubes had been filled. But a toothpaste cap-screwer is never paid very much money, and poor Mr. Bucket, however hard he worked, and however fast he screwed on the caps, was never able to make enough to buy one-half of the things that so large a family needed. There wasn't even enough money to buy proper food for them all. The only meals they could afford were bread and margarine for breakfast, boiled potatoes and cabbage for lunch, and cabbage soup for supper. Sundays were a bit better. They all looked forward to Sundays because then, although they had exactly the same, everyone was allowed a second helping.

The Buckets, of course, didn't starve, but every one of them—the two old grandfathers, the two old grandmothers, Charlie's father, Charlie's mother, and especially little Charlie himself—went about from morning till night with a horrible empty feeling in their tummies.

Charlie felt it worst of all. And although his father and

mother often went without their own share of lunch or supper so that they could give it to him, it still wasn't nearly enough for a growing boy. He desperately wanted something more filling and satisfying than cabbage and cabbage soup. The one thing he longed for more than anything else was . . . CHOCOLATE.

Walking to school in the mornings, Charlie could see great slabs of chocolate piled up high in the shop windows, and he would stop and stare and press his nose against the glass, his mouth watering like mad. Many times a day, he would see other children taking creamy candy bars out of their pockets and munching them greedily, and *that*, of course, was *pure* torture.

Only once a year, on his birthday, did Charlie Bucket ever get to taste a bit of chocolate. The whole family saved up their money for that special occasion, and when the great day arrived, Charlie was always presented with one small chocolate bar to eat all by himself. And each time he received it, on those marvelous birthday mornings, he would place it carefully in a small wooden box that he owned, and treasure it as though it were a bar of solid gold; and for the next few days, he would allow himself only to look at it, but never to touch it. Then at last, when he could stand it no longer, he would peel back a *tiny* bit of the paper wrapping at one corner to expose a *tiny* bit of chocolate, and then he would take a *tiny* nibble—just enough to allow the lovely sweet taste to spread out slowly over his tongue. The next day, he would take another tiny nibble, and so on, and so on. And in this way, Charlie would make his ten-cent bar of birthday chocolate last him for more than a month.

But I haven't yet told you about the one awful thing that tortured little Charlie, the lover of chocolate, more than *anything* else. This thing, for him, was far, far worse than seeing slabs of chocolate in the shop windows or watching other children munching creamy candy bars right in front of him. It was the most terrible torturing thing you could imagine, and it was this:

In the town itself, actually within *sight* of the house in which Charlie lived, there was an ENORMOUS CHOCOLATE FACTORY!

Just imagine that!

And it wasn't simply an ordinary enormous chocolate factory, either. It was the largest and most famous in the whole world! It was WONKA'S FACTORY, owned by a man called Mr. Willy Wonka, the greatest inventor and maker of chocolates that there has ever been. And what a tremendous, marvelous place it was! It had huge iron gates leading in to it, and a high wall surrounding it, and smoke belching from its chimneys, and strange whizzing sounds coming from deep inside it. And outside the walls, for half a mile around in every direction, the air was scented with the heavy rich smell of melting chocolate!

Twice a day, on his way to and from school, little Charlie Bucket had to walk right past the gates of the factory. And every time he went by, he would begin to walk very, very slowly, and he would hold his nose high in the air and take long deep sniffs of the gorgeous chocolatey smell all around him.

Oh, how he loved that smell!

And oh, how he wished he could go inside the factory and see what it was like!

2

Mr. Willy Wonka's Factory

In the evenings, after he had finished his supper of watery cabbage soup, Charlie always went into the room of his four grandparents to listen to their stories, and then afterwards to say good night.

Every one of these old people was over ninety. They were as shriveled as prunes, and as bony as skeletons, and throughout the day, until Charlie made his appearance, they lay huddled in their one bed, two at either end, with nightcaps on to keep their heads warm, dozing the time away with nothing to do. But as soon as they heard the door opening, and heard Charlie's voice saying, "Good evening, Grandpa Joe and Grandma Josephine, and Grandpa George and Grandma Georgina," then all four of them would suddenly sit up, and their old wrinkled faces would light up with smiles of pleasure—and the talking would begin. For they loved this little boy. He was the only bright thing in their lives, and his evening visits were something that they looked forward to all day long. Often, Charlie's mother and father would come in as well, and stand by the door, listening to the stories that the old people told; and thus, for perhaps half an hour every night, this room would become a happy place, and the whole family would forget that it was hungry and poor.

One evening, when Charlie went in to see his grandparents, he said to them, "Is it *really* true that Wonka's

Chocolate Factory is the biggest in the world?"

"*True?*" cried all four of them at once. "Of course it's true! Good heavens, didn't you know *that*? It's about *fifty* times as big as any other!"

"And is Mr. Willy Wonka *really* the cleverest chocolate maker in the world?"

"My *dear* boy," said Grandpa Joe, raising himself up a little higher on his pillow, "Mr. Willy Wonka is the most *amazing,* the most *fantastic,* the most *extraordinary* chocolate maker the world has ever seen! I thought *everybody* knew that!"

"I knew he was famous, Grandpa Joe, and I knew he was very clever. . . ."

"*Clever!*" cried the old man. "He's more than that! He's a *magician* with chocolate! He can make *anything*— anything he wants! Isn't that a fact, my dears?"

The other three old people nodded their heads slowly up and down, and said, "*Absolutely* true. *Just* as true as can be."

And Grandpa Joe said, "You mean to say I've never *told* you about Mr. Willy Wonka and his factory?"

"Never," answered little Charlie.

"Good heavens above! I don't know what's the matter with me!"

"Will you tell me now, Grandpa Joe, please?"

"I certainly will. Sit down beside me on the bed, my dear, and listen carefully."

Grandpa Joe was the oldest of the four grandparents. He was ninety-six and a half, and that is just about as old as anybody can be. Like all extremely old people, he was delicate and weak, and throughout the day he spoke very little. But in the evenings, when Charlie, his beloved grandson, was in the room, he seemed in some marvelous way to grow quite young again. All his tiredness fell away from him, and he became as eager and excited as a young boy.

"Oh, what a man he is, this Mr. Willy Wonka!" cried Grandpa Joe. "Did you know, for example, that he has himself invented more than two hundred new kinds of candy bars, each with a different center, each far sweeter and creamier and more delicious than anything the other chocolate factories can make!"

"Perfectly true!" cried Grandma Josephine. "And he sends them to *all* the four corners of the earth! Isn't that so, Grandpa Joe?"

"It is, my dear, it is. And to all the kings and presidents of the world as well. But it isn't only candy bars that he makes. Oh, dear me, no! He has some really *fantastic* inventions up his sleeve, Mr. Willy Wonka has! Did you know that he's invented a way of making chocolate ice cream so that it stays cold for hours and hours without being in the icebox?

You can even leave it lying in the sun all morning on a hot day and it won't go runny!"

"But that's *impossible*!" said little Charlie, staring at his grandfather.

"Of course it's impossible!" cried Grandpa Joe. "It's completely *absurd*! But Mr. Willy Wonka has done it!"

"Quite right!" the others agreed, nodding their heads. "Mr. Wonka has done it."

"And then again," Grandpa Joe went on, speaking very slowly now so that Charlie wouldn't miss a word, "Mr. Willy Wonka can make marshmallows that taste of violets, and rich caramels that change color every ten seconds as you suck them, and little feathery sweets that melt away deliciously the moment you put them between your lips. He can make chewing gum that never loses its taste, and candy balloons that you can blow up to enormous sizes before you pop them with a pin and gobble them up. And, by a most secret method, he can make lovely blue birds' eggs with black spots on them, and when you put one of these in your mouth, it gradually gets smaller and smaller until suddenly there is nothing left except a tiny little pink sugary baby bird sitting on the tip of your tongue."

Grandpa Joe paused and ran the point of his tongue slowly over his lips. "It makes my mouth water just *thinking* about it," he said.

"Mine, too," said little Charlie. "But *please* go on."

While they were talking, Mr. and Mrs. Bucket, Charlie's mother and father, had come quietly into the room, and now both were standing just inside the door, listening.

"Tell Charlie about that crazy Indian prince," said Grandma Josephine. "He'd like to hear that."

"You mean Prince Pondicherry?" said Grandpa Joe, and he began chuckling with laughter.

"*Completely* dotty!" said Grandpa George.

"But *very* rich," said Grandma Georgina.

"What did he do?" asked Charlie eagerly.

"Listen," said Grandpa Joe, "and I'll tell you."

3

Mr. Wonka and the Indian Prince

"Prince Pondicherry wrote a letter to Mr. Willy Wonka," said Grandpa Joe, "and asked him to come all the way out to India and build him a colossal palace entirely out of chocolate."

"Did Mr. Wonka do it, Grandpa?"

"He did, indeed. And what a palace it was! It had one hundred rooms, and *everything* was made of either dark or light chocolate! The bricks were chocolate, and the cement holding them together was chocolate, and the windows were chocolate, and all the walls and ceilings were made of chocolate, so were the carpets and the pictures and the furniture and the beds; and when you turned on the taps in the bathroom, hot chocolate came pouring out.

"When it was all finished, Mr. Wonka said to Prince Pondicherry, 'I warn you, though, it won't last very long, so you'd better start eating it right away.'

"'Nonsense!' shouted the Prince. 'I'm not going to eat my palace! I'm not even going to nibble the staircase or lick the walls! I'm going to *live* in it!'

"But Mr. Wonka was right, of course, because soon after this, there came a very hot day with a boiling sun, and the whole palace began to melt, and then it sank slowly to the ground, and the crazy prince, who was dozing in the living room at the time, woke up to find himself swimming around in a huge brown sticky lake of chocolate."

Little Charlie sat very still on the edge of the bed, staring at his grandfather. Charlie's face was bright, and his eyes were stretched so wide you could see the whites all around. "Is all this *really* true?" he asked. "Or are you pulling my leg?"

"It's true!" cried all four of the old people at once. "Of course it's true! Ask anyone you like!"

"And I'll tell you something else that's true," said Grandpa Joe, and now he leaned closer to Charlie, and lowered his voice to a soft, secret whisper. *"Nobody . . . ever . . . comes . . . out!"*

"Out of where?" asked Charlie.

"And . . . nobody . . . ever . . . goes . . . in!"

"In *where*?" cried Charlie.

"Wonka's factory, of course!"

"Grandpa, what *do* you mean?"

"I mean *workers,* Charlie."

"Workers?"

"All factories," said Grandpa Joe, "have workers streaming in and out of the gates in the mornings and evenings —except Wonka's! Have *you* ever seen a single person going into that place—or coming out?"

Little Charlie looked slowly around at each of the four old faces, one after the other, and they all looked back at him. They were friendly smiling faces, but they were also quite serious. There was no sign of joking or leg-pulling on any of them.

"Well? Have *you*?" asked Grandpa Joe.

"I . . . I really don't know, Grandpa," Charlie stammered. "Whenever *I* walk past the factory, the gates seem to be closed."

"Exactly!" said Grandpa Joe.

"But there *must* be people working there. . . ."

"Not *people,* Charlie. Not *ordinary* people, anyway."

"Then who?" cried Charlie.

"Ah-ha. . . . That's it, you see. . . . That's another of Mr. Willy Wonka's clevernesses."

"Charlie, dear," Mrs. Bucket called out from where she was standing by the door, "it's time for bed. That's enough for tonight."

"But mother, I *must* hear. . . ."

"Tomorrow, my darling. . . ."

"That's right," said Grandpa Joe, "I'll tell you the rest of it tomorrow evening."

4

The Secret Workers

THE NEXT EVENING, Grandpa Joe went on with his story.

"You see, Charlie," he said, "not so very long ago there used to be thousands of people working in Mr. Willy Wonka's factory. Then one day, all of a sudden, Mr. Wonka had to ask *every single one of them* to leave, to go home, never to come back."

"But why?" asked Charlie.

"Because of spies."

"Spies?"

"Yes. All the other chocolate makers, you see, had begun to grow jealous of the wonderful candies that Mr. Wonka was making, and they started sending in spies to steal his secret recipes. The spies took jobs in the Wonka factory, pretending that they were ordinary workers, and while they were there, each one of them found out exactly how a certain special thing was made."

"And did they go back to their own factories and tell?" asked Charlie.

"They must have," answered Grandpa Joe, "because

soon after that, Fickelgruber's factory started making an ice cream that would never melt, even in the hottest sun. Then Mr. Prodnose's factory came out with a chewing gum that never lost its flavor however much you chewed it. And then Mr. Slugworth's factory began making candy balloons that you could blow up to huge sizes before you popped them with a pin and gobbled them up. And so on, and so on. And Mr. Willy Wonka tore his beard and shouted, 'This is terrible! I shall be ruined! There are spies everywhere! I shall have to close the factory!'"

"But he didn't do that!" Charlie said.

"Oh, yes he did. He told *all* the workers that he was sorry, but they would have to go home. Then, he shut the main gates and fastened them with a chain. And suddenly, Wonka's giant chocolate factory became silent and deserted. The chimneys stopped smoking, the machines stopped whirring, and from then on, not a single chocolate or candy was made. Not a soul went in or out, and even Mr. Willy Wonka himself disappeared completely.

"Months and months went by," Grandpa Joe went on, "but still the factory remained closed. And everybody said, 'Poor Mr. Wonka. He was so nice. And he made such marvelous things. But he's finished now. It's all over.'

"Then something astonishing happened. One day, early in the morning, thin columns of white smoke were seen to be coming out of the tops of the tall chimneys of the factory! People in the town stopped and stared. 'What's going on?' they cried. 'Someone's lit the furnaces! Mr. Wonka must be opening up again!' They ran to the gates, expecting to see them wide open and Mr. Wonka standing there to welcome his workers back.

"But no! The great iron gates were still locked and chained as securely as ever, and Mr. Wonka was nowhere to be seen.

"'But the factory *is* working!' the people shouted. 'Listen! You can hear the machines! They're all whirring again! And you can smell the smell of melting chocolate in the air!'"

Grandpa Joe leaned forward and laid a long bony finger on Charlie's knee, and he said softly, "But most mysterious of all, Charlie, were the shadows in the windows of the factory. The people standing on the street outside could see small dark shadows moving about behind the frosted glass windows."

"Shadows of whom?" said Charlie quickly.

"That's exactly what everybody else wanted to know.

"'The place is full of workers!' the people shouted. 'But nobody's gone in! The gates are locked! It's crazy! Nobody ever comes out, either!'

"But there was no question at all," said Grandpa Joe, "that the factory *was* running. And it's gone on running ever since, for these last ten years. What's more, the chocolates and candies it's been turning out have become more fantastic and delicious all the time. And of course *now,* when Mr. Wonka invents some new and wonderful candy, neither Mr. Fickelgruber nor Mr. Prodnose nor Mr. Slugworth nor anybody else is able to copy it. No spies can go into the factory to find out how it is made."

"But Grandpa, *who,*" cried Charlie, "*who* is Mr. Wonka using to do all the work in the factory?"

"Nobody knows, Charlie."

"But that's *absurd!* Hasn't someone asked Mr. Wonka?"

"Nobody sees him any more. He never comes out. The only things that come out of that place are chocolates and candies. They come out through a special trap door in the wall, all packed and addressed, and they are picked up every day by Post Office trucks."

"But Grandpa, what *sort* of people are they that work in there?"

"My dear boy," said Grandpa Joe, "that is one of the great mysteries of the chocolate-making world. We know only one thing about them. They are very small. The faint shadows that sometimes appear behind the windows, especially late at night when the lights are on, are those of *tiny* people, people no taller than my knee. . . ."

"There aren't any such people," Charlie said.

Just then, Mr. Bucket, Charlie's father, came into the room. He was home from the toothpaste factory, and he was waving an evening newspaper rather excitedly. "Have you heard the news?" he cried. He held up the paper so that they could see the huge headline. The headline said:

WONKA FACTORY TO BE OPENED AT LAST TO LUCKY FEW

5
The Golden Tickets

"YOU MEAN people are actually going to be allowed to go inside the factory?" cried Grandpa Joe. "Read us what it says—quickly!"

"All right," said Mr. Bucket, smoothing out the newspaper. "Listen."

Evening Bulletin

Mr. Willy Wonka, the candy-making genius whom nobody has seen for the last ten years, sent out the following notice today:

I, Willy Wonka, have decided to allow five children —just *five,* mind you, and no more—to visit my factory this year. These lucky five will be shown around personally by me, and they will be allowed to see all the secrets and the magic of my factory. Then, at the end of the tour, as a special present, all of them will be given enough chocolates and candies to last them for the rest of their lives! So watch out for the Golden Tickets! Five Golden Tickets have been printed on golden paper, and these five Golden Tickets have been hidden underneath the ordinary wrapping paper of five ordinary candy bars. These five candy bars may be anywhere—in any shop in any street in any town in any country in the world—upon any counter where Wonka's candies are sold. And the five lucky finders of these five Golden Tickets are the *only* ones who will be allowed to visit my factory and see what it's like *now* inside! Good luck to you all, and happy hunting! (Signed Willy Wonka.)

"The man's dotty!" muttered Grandma Josephine.

"He's brilliant!" cried Grandpa Joe. "He's a magician! Just imagine what will happen now! The whole world will be searching for those Golden Tickets! Everyone will be buying Wonka's candy bars in the hope of finding one! He'll sell more than ever before! Oh, how exciting it would be to find one!"

"And all the chocolate and candies that you could eat for the rest of your life—*free!*" said Grandpa George. "Just imagine that!"

"They'd have to deliver them in a truck!" said Grandma Georgina.

"It makes me quite ill to think of it," said Grandma Josephine.

"Nonsense!" cried Grandpa Joe. "Wouldn't it be *something,* Charlie, to open a bar of candy and see a Golden Ticket glistening inside!"

"It certainly would, Grandpa. But there isn't a hope," Charlie said sadly. "I only get one bar a year."

"You never know, darling," said Grandma Georgina. "It's your birthday next week. You have as much chance as anybody else."

"I'm afraid that simply isn't true," said Grandpa George. "The kids who are going to find the Golden Tickets are the ones who can afford to buy candy bars every day. Our Charlie gets only one a year. There isn't a hope."

6
The First Two Finders

THE VERY NEXT DAY, the first Golden Ticket was found. The finder was a boy called Augustus Gloop, and Mr. Bucket's evening newspaper carried a large picture of him on the front page. The picture showed a nine-year-old boy who was so enormously fat he looked as though he had been blown up with a powerful pump. Great flabby folds of fat bulged out from every part of his body, and his face was like a monstrous ball of dough with two small greedy curranty eyes peering out upon the world. The town in which Augustus Gloop lived, the newspaper said, had gone wild with excitement over their hero. Flags were flying from all the windows, children had been given a holiday from school, and a parade was being organized in honor of the famous youth.

"I just *knew* Augustus would find a Golden Ticket," his mother had told the newspapermen. "He eats *so many* candy bars a day that it was almost *impossible* for him *not* to find one. Eating is his hobby, you know. That's *all* he's interested in. But still, that's better than being a *hooligan* and shooting off *zip guns* and things like that in his spare time, isn't it? And what I always say is, he wouldn't go on eating like he does unless he *needed* nourishment, would he? It's all *vitamins,* anyway. What a *thrill* it will be for him to visit Mr. Wonka's marvelous factory! We're just as *proud* as can be!"

"What a revolting woman," said Grandma Josephine.

"And what a repulsive boy," said Grandma Georgina.

"Only four Golden Tickets left," said Grandpa George. "I wonder who'll get *those.*"

And now the whole country, indeed, the whole world, seemed suddenly to be caught up in a mad candy-buying spree, everybody searching frantically for those precious remaining tickets. Fully grown women were seen going into sweetshops and buying ten Wonka candy bars at a time, then tearing off the wrappers on the spot and peering eagerly underneath for a glint of golden paper. Children were taking hammers and smashing their piggy banks and running out to the shops with handfuls of money. In one city, a famous gangster robbed a bank of five thousand dollars and spent the whole lot on candy bars that same afternoon. And when the police entered his house to arrest him, they found him sitting on the floor amidst mountains of candy, ripping off the wrappers with the blade of a long dagger. In far-off Russia, a woman called Charlotte Russe claimed to have found the second ticket, but it turned out to be a clever fake. In England, the famous scientist, Professor Foulbody, invented a machine which would tell you at once, without opening the wrapper of a candy bar, whether or not there was a Golden Ticket hidden underneath it. The machine had a mechanical arm that shot out with tremendous force and grabbed hold of anything that had the slightest bit of gold inside it, and for a moment, it looked like the answer to everything. But unfortunately, while the Professor was showing off the machine to the public at the candy counter of a large department store, the mechanical arm shot out and made a grab for the gold filling in the back tooth of a duchess who was standing nearby. There was an ugly scene, and the machine was smashed by the crowd.

Suddenly, on the day before Charlie Bucket's birthday, the newspapers announced that the second Golden Ticket had been found. The lucky person was a small girl called Veruca Salt who lived with her rich parents in a great city far away. Once again, Mr. Bucket's evening newspaper carried a big picture of the finder. She was sitting between her beaming father and mother in the living room of their house, waving the Golden Ticket above her head, and grinning from ear to ear.

Veruca's father, Mr. Salt, had eagerly explained to the newspapermen exactly how the ticket was found. "You see, fellers," he had said, "as soon as my little girl told me that she simply *had* to have one of those Golden Tickets, I went out into the town and started buying up all the Wonka candy bars I could lay my hands on. *Thousands* of them, I must have bought. *Hundreds* of thousands! Then I had them loaded onto trucks and sent directly to my *own* factory. I'm in the peanut business, you see, and I've got about a hundred women working for me over at my joint, shelling peanuts for roasting and salting. That's what they do all day long, those women, they sit there shelling peanuts. So I says to them, 'Okay, girls,' I says, 'from now on, you can stop shelling peanuts and start shelling the wrappers off these crazy candy bars instead!' And they did. I had every worker in the place yanking the paper off those bars of chocolate full speed ahead from morning till night.

"But three days went by, and we had no luck. Oh, it was terrible! My little Veruca got more and more upset each day, and every time I went home she would scream at me, *'Where's my Golden Ticket! I want my Golden Ticket!'* And she would lie for hours on the floor, kicking and yelling in the most disturbing way. Well, sir, I just hated to see my little girl feeling unhappy like that, so I vowed I would keep up the search until I'd got her what she wanted. Then suddenly . . . on the evening of the fourth day, one of my women workers yelled, 'I've got it! A Golden Ticket!' And I said, 'Give it to me, quick!' and she did, and I rushed it home and gave it to my darling Veruca, and now she's all smiles, and we have a happy home once again."

"That's even worse than the fat boy," said Grandma Josephine.

"She needs a real good spanking," said Grandma Georgina.

"I don't think the girl's father played it quite fair, Grandpa, do you?" Charlie murmured.

"He spoils her," Grandpa Joe said. "And no good can ever come from spoiling a child like that, Charlie, you mark my words."

"Come to bed, my darling," said Charlie's mother. "Tomorrow's your birthday, don't forget that, so I expect you'll be up early to open your present."

"A Wonka candy bar!" cried Charlie. "It is a Wonka candy bar, isn't it?"

"Yes, my love," his mother said. "Of course it is."

"Oh, wouldn't it be wonderful if I found the third Golden Ticket inside it?" Charlie said.

"Bring it in here when you get it," Grandpa Joe said. "Then we can all watch you taking off the wrapper."

7
Charlie's Birthday

"HAPPY BIRTHDAY!" cried the four old grandparents, as Charlie came into their room early the next morning.

Charlie smiled nervously and sat down on the edge of the bed. He was holding his present, his only present, very carefully in his two hands. WONKA'S WHIPPLE-SCRUMPTIOUS FUDGEMALLOW DELIGHT, it said on the wrapper.

The four old people, two at either end of the bed,

propped themselves up on their pillows and stared with anxious eyes at the candy bar in Charlie's hands.

Mr. and Mrs. Bucket came in and stood at the foot of the bed, watching Charlie.

The room became silent. Everybody was waiting now for Charlie to start opening his present. Charlie looked down at the candy bar. He ran his fingers slowly back and forth along the length of it, stroking it lovingly, and the shiny paper wrapper made little sharp crackly noises in the quiet room.

Then Mrs. Bucket said gently, "You mustn't be too disappointed, my darling, if you don't find what you're looking for underneath that wrapper. You really can't expect to be as lucky as all that."

"She's quite right," Mr. Bucket said.

Charlie didn't say anything.

"After all," Grandma Josephine said, "in the whole wide world there are only three tickets left to be found."

"The thing to remember," Grandma Georgina said, "is that whatever happens, you'll still have the bar of candy."

"Wonka's Whipple-Scrumptious Fudgemallow Delight!" cried Grandpa George. "It's the best of them all! You'll just *love* it!"

"Yes," Charlie whispered. "I know."

"Just forget all about those Golden Tickets and enjoy the candy," Grandpa Joe said. "Why don't you do that?"

They all knew it was ridiculous to expect this one poor little candy bar to have a magic ticket inside it, and they were trying as gently and as kindly as they could to prepare Charlie for the disappointment. But there was one other thing that the grownups also knew, and it was this: that however *small* the chance might be of striking lucky, *the chance was there.*

The chance *had* to be there.

This particular candy bar had as much chance as any other of having a Golden Ticket.

And that was why all the grandparents and parents in the room were actually just as tense and excited as Charlie was, although they were pretending to be very calm.

"You'd better go ahead and open it up, or you'll be late for school," Grandpa Joe said.

"You might as well get it over with," Grandpa George said.

"Open it, my dear," Grandma Georgina said. "Please open it. You're making me jumpy."

Very slowly, Charlie's fingers began to tear open one small corner of the wrapping paper.

The old people in the bed all leaned forward, craning their scraggy necks.

Then suddenly, as though he couldn't bear the suspense any longer, Charlie tore the wrapper right down the middle . . . and on to his lap, there fell . . . a light-brown creamy-colored chocolate candy bar.

There was no sign of a Golden Ticket anywhere.

"Well—that's *that!*" said Grandpa Joe brightly. "It's just what we expected."

Charlie looked up. Four kind old faces were watching him intently from the bed. He smiled at them, a small sad smile, and then he shrugged his shoulders and picked up the candy bar and held it out to his mother, and said, "Here Mother, have a bit. We'll share it. I want everybody to taste it."

"Certainly not!" his mother said.

And the others all cried, "No, no! We wouldn't dream of it! It's *all* yours!"

"Please," begged Charlie, turning around and offering it to Grandpa Joe.

But neither he nor anyone else would take even a tiny bite.

"It's time to go to school, my darling," Mrs. Bucket said, putting an arm around Charlie's skinny shoulders. "Come on, or you'll be late."

8
Two More Golden Tickets Found

THAT EVENING, Mr. Bucket's newspaper announced the finding of not only the third Golden Ticket, but the fourth as well. TWO GOLDEN TICKETS FOUND TODAY, screamed the headlines. ONLY ONE MORE LEFT.

"All right," said Grandpa Joe, when the whole family was gathered in the old people's room after supper, "let's hear who found them."

"The third ticket," read Mr. Bucket, holding the newspaper up close to his face because his eyes were bad and he couldn't afford glasses, "the third Ticket was found by a Miss Violet Beauregarde. There was great excitement in the Beauregarde household when our reporter arrived to interview the lucky young lady—cameras were clicking and flashbulbs were flashing and people were pushing and jostling and trying to get a bit closer to the famous girl. And the famous girl was standing on a chair in the living-room waving the Golden Ticket madly at arm's length as though she were flagging a taxi. She was talking very fast and very loudly to everyone, but it was not easy to hear all that she said because she was chewing so ferociously upon a piece of gum at the same time.

"'I'm a gumchewer, normally,' she shouted, 'but when I heard about these ticket things of Mr. Wonka's, I laid off the gum and switched to candy bars in the hope of striking lucky. *Now*, of course, I'm right back on gum. I just *adore* gum. I can't do without it. I munch it all day long except for a few minutes at mealtimes when I take it out and stick it behind my ear for safekeeping. To tell you the honest truth, I simply wouldn't feel *comfortable* if I didn't have that little wedge of gum to chew on every moment of the day, I really wouldn't. My mother says it's not ladylike and it looks ugly to see a girl's jaws going up and down like mine do all the time, but I don't agree. And who's she to criticize, anyway, because if you ask me, I'd say that *her* jaws are going up and down almost as much as mine are just from *yelling* at me every minute of the day.'

"'Now, Violet,' Mrs. Beauregarde said from a far corner of the room where she was standing on the piano to avoid being trampled by the mob.

"'All right, Mother, keep your hair on!' Miss Beauregarde shouted. 'And now,' she went on, turning to the reporters again, 'it may interest you to know that this piece of gum I'm chewing right at this moment is one I've been working on for over *three months solid*. That's a record, that is. It's beaten the record held by my best friend, Miss Cornelia Prinzmetel. And was she mad! It's my most treasured possession now, this piece of gum is. At nights, I just stick it on the end of the bedpost, and it's as good as ever in the mornings—a bit hard at first, maybe, but it soon softens up again after I've given it a few good chews. Before I started chewing for the world record, I used to change my piece of gum once a day. I used to do it in our elevator on the way home from school. Why the elevator? Because I liked sticking the gooey piece that I'd just finished with on to one of the elevator buttons. Then the next person who came along and pressed the button got my old gum on the end of his or her finger. Ha-ha! And what a racket they kicked up, some of them. You get the best results with women who have expensive gloves on. Oh yes, I'm thrilled to be going to Mr. Wonka's factory. And I understand that afterwards he's going to give me enough gum to last me for the rest of my whole life. Whoopee! Hooray!"

"*Beastly* girl," said Grandma Josephine.

"Despicable!" said Grandma Georgina. "She'll come to a sticky end one day, chewing all that gum, you see if she doesn't."

"And who got the fourth Golden Ticket, Daddy?" Charlie asked.

"Now, let me see," said Mr. Bucket, peering at the newspaper again. "Ah yes, here we are. The fourth Golden Ticket," he read, "was found by a boy called Mike Teavee."

"Another bad lot, I'll be bound," muttered Grandma Josephine.

"Don't interrupt, Grandma," said Mrs. Bucket.

"The Teavee household," said Mr. Bucket, going on with his reading, "was crammed, like all the others, with excited visitors when our reporter arrived, but young Mike Teavee, the lucky winner, seemed extremely annoyed by the whole business. 'Can't you fools see I'm watching television?' he said angrily, 'I wish you wouldn't interrupt!'

"The nine-year-old boy was seated before an enormous television set, with his eyes glued to the screen, and he was watching a film in which one bunch of gangsters was shooting up another bunch of gangsters with machine guns. Mike Teavee himself had no less than eighteen toy pistols of various sizes hanging from belts around his body, and every now and again he would leap up into the air and fire off half a dozen rounds from one or another of these weapons.

"'Quiet!' he shouted, when someone tried to ask him a question. 'Didn't I *tell* you not to interrupt! This show's an absolute whiz-banger! It's terrific! I watch it every day. I watch all of them every day, even the crummy ones, where there's no shooting. I like the gangsters best.

They're terrific, those gangsters! Especially when they start pumping each other full of lead, or flashing the old stilettos, or giving each other the one-two-three with their knuckle-dusters! Oh boy, what wouldn't I give to be doing that myself! It's the *life*, I tell you! It's terrific!'"

"That's quite enough!" snapped Grandma Josephine. "I can't *bear* to listen to it!"

"Nor me," said Grandma Georgina. "Do *all* children behave like this nowadays—like these brats we've been hearing about?"

"Of course not," said Mr. Bucket, smiling at the old lady in the bed. "Some do, of course. In fact, quite a lot of them do. But not *all*."

"And now there's only *one ticket left!*" said Grandpa George.

"Quite so," sniffed Grandma Georgina. "And just as sure as I'll be having cabbage soup for supper tomorrow, that ticket'll go to some nasty little beast who doesn't deserve it!"

9
Grandpa Joe Takes a Gamble

THE NEXT DAY, when Charlie came home from school and went in to see his grandparents, he found that only Grandpa Joe was awake. The other three were all snoring loudly.

"Ssshh!" whispered Grandpa Joe, and he beckoned Charlie to come closer. Charlie tiptoed over and stood beside the bed. The old man gave Charlie a sly grin, and then he started rummaging under his pillow with one hand; and when the hand came out again, there was an ancient leather purse clutched in the fingers. Under cover of the bedclothes, the old man opened the purse and tipped it upside down. Out fell a single silver ten-cent piece. "It's my secret hoard," he whispered. "The others don't know I've got it. And now, you and I are going to have one more fling at finding that last ticket. How about it, eh? But you'll have to help me."

"Are you *sure* you want to spend your money on that, Grandpa?" Charlie whispered.

"Of course I'm sure!" spluttered the old man excitedly. "Don't stand there arguing! I'm just as crazy as you are to find that ticket! Here—take the money and run down the street to the nearest store and buy the first Wonka candy bar you see and bring it straight back to me, and we'll open it together."

Charlie took the little silver coin, and slipped quickly out of the room. In five minutes, he was back.

"Have you got it?" whispered Grandpa Joe, his eyes shining with excitement.

Charlie nodded and held out the bar of candy. WONKA'S NUTTY CRUNCH SURPRISE, it said on the wrapper.

"Good!" the old man whispered, sitting up in the bed and rubbing his hands. "Now—come over here and sit close to me and we'll open it together. Are you ready?"

"Yes," Charlie said. "I'm ready."

"All right. You tear off the first bit."

"No," Charlie said, "you paid for it. You do it all."

The old man's fingers were trembling most terribly as they fumbled with the candy bar. "We don't have a hope, really," he whispered, giggling a bit. "You do know we don't have a hope, don't you?"

"Yes," Charlie said. "I know that."

They looked at each other, and both started giggling nervously.

"Mind you," said Grandpa Joe, "there is just that *tiny* chance that it *might* be the one, don't you agree?"

"Yes," Charlie said. "Of course. Why don't you open it Grandpa?"

"All in good time, my boy, all in good time. Which end do you think I ought to open first?"

"That corner. The one furthest from you. Just tear off a *tiny* bit, but not quite enough for us to see anything."

"Like that?" said the old man.

"Yes. Now a little bit more."

"You finish it," said Grandpa Joe. "I'm too nervous."

"No, Grandpa. You must do it yourself."

"Very well, then. Here goes." He tore off the wrapper.

They both stared at what lay underneath.

It was a bar of candy—nothing more.

All at once, they both saw the funny side of the whole thing, and they burst into peals of laughter.

"What the heck's going on!" cried Grandma Josephine, waking up suddenly.

"Nothing," said Grandpa Joe. "You go on back to sleep."

10
The Family Begins to Starve

DURING THE NEXT TWO WEEKS, the weather turned very cold. First came the snow. It began very suddenly one morning just as Charlie Bucket was getting dressed for school. Standing by the window, he saw the huge flakes drifting slowly down out of an icy sky that was the color of steel.

By evening, it lay four feet deep around the tiny house, and Mr. Bucket had to dig a path from the front door to the road.

After the snow, there came a freezing gale that blew for days and days without stopping. And oh, how bitter cold it was! Everything that Charlie touched seemed to be made of ice, and each time he stepped outside the door, the wind was like a knife on his cheek.

Inside the house, little jets of freezing air came rushing in through the sides of the windows and under the doors, and there was no place to go to escape them. The four old ones lay silent and huddled in their bed, trying to keep the cold out of their bones. The excitement over the Golden Tickets had long since been forgotten. Nobody in the family gave a thought now to anything except the two vital problems of trying to keep warm and trying to get enough to eat.

There is something about very cold weather that gives one an enormous appetite. Most of us find ourselves beginning to crave rich steaming stews and hot apple pies and all kinds of delicious warming dishes; and because we are all a great deal luckier than we realize, we usually get what we want—or near enough. But Charlie Bucket never got what he wanted because the family couldn't afford it, and as the cold weather went on and on, he became ravenously and desperately hungry. Both bars of candy, the birthday one and the one Grandpa Joe had bought, had long since been nibbled away, and all he got now were those thin, cabbagy meals three times a day.

Then all at once, the meals became even thinner.

The reason for this was that the toothpaste factory, the place where Mr. Bucket worked, suddenly went bust and had to close down. Quickly, Mr. Bucket tried to get another job. But he had no luck. In the end, the only way in which he managed to earn a few pennies was by shoveling snow in the streets. But it wasn't enough to buy even a quarter of the food that seven people needed. The situation became desperate. Breakfast was a single slice of bread for each person now, and lunch was maybe half a boiled potato.

Slowly but surely, everybody in the house began to starve.

And every day, little Charlie Bucket, trudging through the snow on his way to school, would have to pass Mr. Willy Wonka's giant chocolate factory. And every day, as he came near to it, he would lift his small pointed nose high in the air and sniff the wonderful sweet smell of melting chocolate. Sometimes, he would stand motionless outside the gates for several minutes on end, taking deep swallowing breaths as though he were trying to *eat* the smell itself.

"That child," said Grandpa Joe, poking his head up from under the blanket one icy morning, "that child has

got to have more food. It doesn't matter about us. We're too old to bother with. But a *growing boy!* He can't go on like this! He's beginning to look like a skeleton!"

"What can one *do*?" murmured Grandma Josephine miserably. "He refuses to take any of ours. I hear his mother tried to slip her own piece of bread onto his plate at breakfast this morning, but he wouldn't touch it. He made her take it back."

"He's a fine little fellow," said Grandpa George. "He deserves better than this."

The cruel weather went on and on.

And every day, Charlie Bucket grew thinner and thinner. His face became frighteningly white and pinched. The skin was drawn so tightly over the cheeks that you could see the shapes of the bones underneath. It seemed doubtful whether he could go on much longer like this without becoming dangerously ill.

And now, very calmly, with that curious wisdom that seems to come so often to small children in times of hardship, he began to make little changes here and there in some of the things that he did, so as to save his strength. In the mornings, he left the house ten minutes earlier so that he could walk slowly to school, without ever having to run. He sat quietly in the classroom during recess, resting himself, while the others rushed outdoors and threw snowballs and wrestled in the snow. Everything he did now, he did slowly and carefully, to prevent exhaustion.

Then one afternoon, walking back home with the icy wind in his face (and incidentally feeling hungrier than he had ever felt before), his eye was caught suddenly by a piece of paper that was lying in the gutter, in the snow.

The paper was of a greenish color, and there was something vaguely familiar about it. Charlie stepped off the curb and bent down to examine it. Part of it was buried under the snow, but he saw at once what it was.

It was a dollar bill!

Quickly he looked around him.

Had somebody just dropped it?

No—that was impossible because of the way part of it was buried.

Several people went hurrying past him on the sidewalk, their chins sunk deep in the collars of their coats, their feet crunching in the snow. None of them was searching for any money; none of them was taking the slightest notice of the small boy crouching in the gutter.

Then was it *his,* this dollar?

Could he *have* it?

Carefully, Charlie pulled it out from under the snow. It was damp and dirty, but otherwise perfect.

A WHOLE dollar!

He held it tightly between his shivering fingers, gazing down at it. It meant one thing to him at that moment, only *one* thing. It meant FOOD.

Automatically, Charlie turned and began moving toward the nearest shop. It was only ten paces away . . . it was a newspaper and stationery store, the kind that sells almost everything, including candy and cigars . . . and what he would *do,* he whispered quickly to himself . . . he would buy one luscious bar of candy and eat it *all* up, every bit of it, right then and there . . . and the rest of the money he would take straight back home and give to his mother.

11
The Miracle

CHARLIE ENTERED THE STORE and laid the damp dollar bill on the counter.

"One Wonka's Whipple-Scrumptious Fudgemallow Delight," he said, remembering how much he had loved the one he had on his birthday.

The man behind the counter looked fat and well-fed. He had big lips and fat cheeks and a very fat neck. The fat around his neck bulged out all around the top of his collar like a rubber ring. He turned and reached behind him

for the candy bar, then he turned back again and handed it to Charlie. Charlie grabbed it and quickly tore off the wrapper and took an enormous bite. Then he took another . . . and another . . . and oh, the joy of being able to cram large pieces of something sweet and solid into one's mouth! The sheer blissful joy of being able to fill one's mouth with rich solid food!

"You look like you wanted that one, sonny," the shopkeeper said pleasantly.

Charlie nodded, his mouth bulging with chocolate.

The shopkeeper put Charlie's change on the counter. "Take it easy," he said. "It'll give you a gut-ache if you swallow it like that without chewing."

Charlie went on wolfing the candy. He couldn't stop.

And in less than half a minute, the whole thing had disappeared down his throat. He was quite out of breath, but he felt marvelously, extraordinarily happy. He reached out a hand to take the change. Then he paused. His eyes were just above the level of the counter. They were staring at the little silver coins lying there. The coins were all dimes. There were nine of them altogether. Surely it wouldn't matter if he spent just one more. . . .

"I think," he said quietly, "I think . . . I'll have just one more of those candy bars. The same kind as before, please."

"Why not?" the fat shopkeeper said, reaching behind him again and taking another Whipple-Scrumptious Fudgemallow Delight from the shelf. He laid it on the counter.

Charlie picked it up and tore off the wrapper . . . and *suddenly* . . . from underneath the wrapper . . . there came a brilliant flash of gold.

Charlie's heart stood still.

"It's a Golden Ticket!" screamed the shopkeeper, leaping about a foot in the air. "You've got a Golden Ticket! You've found the last Golden Ticket! Hey, what do you know! Come and look at this, everybody! The kid's found Wonka's last Golden Ticket! There it is! It's right there in his hands!"

It seemed as though the shopkeeper might be going to have a fit. "In my shop, too!" he yelled. "He found it right here in my own little shop! Somebody call the newspapers quick and let them know! Watch out now, sonny! Don't tear it as you unwrap it! That thing's precious!"

In a few seconds, there was a crowd of about twenty people clustering around Charlie, and many more were pushing their way in from the street. Everybody wanted to get a look at the Golden Ticket and at the lucky finder.

"Where is it?" somebody shouted. "Hold it up so all of us can see it!"

"There it is, there!" someone else shouted. "He's holding it in his hands! See the gold shining!"

"How did *he* manage to find it, I'd like to know?" a large boy shouted angrily. "*Twenty* bars a day I've been buying for weeks and weeks!"

"Think of all the free stuff he'll be getting too!" another boy said enviously. "A lifetime supply!"

"He'll need it, the skinny little shrimp!" a girl said, laughing.

Charlie hadn't moved. He hadn't even unwrapped the Golden Ticket from around the candy bar. He was standing very still, holding it tightly with both hands while the crowd pushed and shouted all around him. He felt quite dizzy. There was a peculiar floating sensation coming over him, as though he were floating up in the air like a balloon. His feet didn't seem to be touching the ground at all. He could hear his heart thumping away loudly somewhere in his throat.

At that point, he became aware of a hand resting lightly on his shoulder, and when he looked up, he saw a tall man standing over him. "Listen," the man whispered. "I'll buy it from you. I'll give you fifty dollars. How about it, eh? And I'll give you a new bicycle as well. Okay?"

"Are you *crazy*?" shouted a woman who was standing equally close. "Why, I'd give him *five hundred* dollars for that ticket! You want to sell that ticket for five hundred dollars, young man?"

"That's *quite* enough of that!" the fat shopkeeper

shouted, pushing his way through the crowd and taking Charlie firmly by the arm. "Leave the kid alone, will you! Make way there! Let him out!" And to Charlie, as he led him to the door, he whispered, "Don't you let *anybody* have it! Take it straight home, quickly, before you lose it! Run all the way and don't stop till you get there, you understand?"

Charlie nodded.

"You know something," the fat shopkeeper said, pausing a moment and smiling at Charlie, "I have a feeling you needed a break like this. I'm awfully glad you got it. Good luck to you, sonny."

"Thank you," Charlie said, and off he went, running through the snow as fast as his legs would go. And as he flew past Mr. Willy Wonka's factory, he turned and waved at it and sang out, "I'll be seeing you! I'll be seeing you soon!" And five minutes later he arrived at his own home.

12
What It Said on the Golden Ticket

CHARLIE BURST THROUGH the front door, shouting, *"Mother! Mother! Mother!"*

Mrs. Bucket was in the old grandparents' room, serving them their evening soup.

"Mother!" yelled Charlie, rushing in on them like a hur-

ricane. "Look! I've got it! Look, Mother, look! The last Golden Ticket! It's mine! I found some money in the street and I bought two candy bars and the second one had the Golden Ticket and there were *crowds* of people all around me wanting to see it and the shopkeeper rescued me and I ran all the way home and here I am! *IT'S THE FIFTH GOLDEN TICKET, MOTHER, AND I'VE FOUND IT!*"

Mrs. Bucket simply stood and stared, while the four old grandparents, who were sitting up in bed balancing bowls of soup on their laps, all dropped their spoons with a clatter and froze against their pillows.

For about ten seconds there was absolute silence in the room. Nobody dared to speak or move. It was a magic moment.

Then, very softly, Grandpa Joe said, "You're pulling our legs, Charlie, aren't you? You're having a little joke?"

"I am *not*!" cried Charlie, rushing up to the bed and holding out the large and beautiful Golden Ticket for him to see.

Grandpa Joe leaned forward and took a close look, his nose almost touching the ticket. The others watched him, waiting for the verdict.

Then very slowly, with a slow and marvelous grin spreading all over his face, Grandpa Joe lifted his head and looked straight at Charlie. The color was rushing to his cheeks, and his eyes were wide open, shining with joy, and in the center of each eye, right in the very center, in the black pupil, a little spark of wild excitement was slowly dancing. Then the old man took a deep breath, and suddenly, with no warning whatsoever, an explosion seemed to take place inside him. He threw up his arms

and yelled *"Yippeeeeeeeeeeeeeeeeeeeeeeeeeeee!"* And at the same time, his long bony body rose up out of the bed and his bowl of soup went flying into the face of Grandma Josephine, and in one fantastic leap, this old fellow of ninety-six and a half, who hadn't been out of bed these last twenty years, jumped on to the floor and started doing a dance of victory in his pajamas.

"Yippeeeeeeeeee!" he shouted. "Three cheers for Charlie! Hip, hip, hooray!"

At this point, the door opened, and Mr. Bucket walked into the room. He was cold and tired, and he looked it. All day long, he had been shoveling snow in the streets.

"Cripes!" he cried. "What's going on in here?"

It didn't take them long to tell him what had happened.

"I don't believe it!" he said. "It's not possible."

"Show him the ticket, Charlie!" shouted Grandpa Joe, who was still dancing around the floor like a dervish in his striped pajamas. "Show your father the fifth and last Golden Ticket in the world!"

"Let me see it, Charlie," Mr. Bucket said, collapsing into a chair and holding out his hand. Charlie came forward with the precious document.

It was a very beautiful thing, this Golden Ticket, having been made, so it seemed, from a sheet of pure gold hammered out almost to the thinness of paper. On one side of it, printed by some clever method in jet-black letters, was the invitation itself—from Mr. Wonka.

"Read it aloud," said Grandpa Joe, climbing back into bed again at last. "Let's all hear exactly what it says."

Mr. Bucket held the lovely Golden Ticket up close

to his eyes. His hands were trembling slightly, and he seemed to be overcome by the whole business. He took several deep breaths. Then he cleared his throat, and said, "All right, I'll read it. Here we go:

'Greetings to you, the lucky finder of this golden ticket, from Mr. Willy Wonka! I shake you warmly by the hand! Tremendous things are in store for you! Many wonderful surprises await you! For now, I do invite you to come to my factory and be my guest for one whole day—you and all others who are lucky enough to find my Golden Tickets. I, Willy Wonka, will conduct you around the factory myself, showing you everything that there is to see, and afterwards, when it is time to leave, you will be escorted home by a procession of large trucks. These trucks, I can promise you, will be loaded with enough delicious eatables to last you and your entire household for many years. If, at any time thereafter, you should run out of supplies, you have only to come back to the factory and show this Golden Ticket, and I shall be happy to refill your cupboard with whatever you want. In this way, you will be able to keep yourself supplied with tasty morsels for the rest of your life. But this is by no means the most exciting thing that will happen on the day of your visit. I am preparing other surprises that are even more marvelous and more fantastic for you and for all my beloved Golden Ticket holders—mystic and marvelous surprises that will entrance, delight, intrigue, astonish, and perplex you beyond measure. In your wildest

dreams you could not imagine that such things could happen to you! Just wait and see! And now, here are your instructions: The day I have chosen for the visit is the first day in the month of February. On this day, and on no other, you must come to the factory gates at ten o'clock sharp in the morning. Don't be late! And you are allowed to bring with you either one or two members of your own family to look after you and to ensure that you don't get into mischief. One more thing—be certain to have this ticket with you, otherwise you will not be admitted.

(Signed) Willy Wonka.'"

"The first day of *February*!" cried Mrs. Bucket. "But that's *tomorrow*! Today is the last day of January, *I know it is!*"

"Cripes!" said Mr. Bucket. "I think you're right!"

"You're just in time!" shouted Grandpa Joe. "There's not a moment to lose. You must start making preparations at once! Wash your face, comb your hair, scrub your hands, brush your teeth, blow your nose, cut your nails, polish your shoes, iron your shirt, and for heaven's sake, get all that mud off your pants! You must get ready, my boy! You must get ready for the biggest day of your life!"

"Now don't overexcite yourself, Grandpa," Mrs. Bucket said. "And don't fluster poor Charlie. We must all try to keep very calm. Now the first thing to decide is this— who is going to go with Charlie to the factory?"

"*I* will!" shouted Grandpa Joe, leaping out of bed once again. "I'll take him! I'll look after him! You leave it to me!"

Mrs. Bucket smiled at the old man, then she turned to her husband and said, "How about you, dear? Don't you think *you* ought to go?"

"Well . . ." Mr. Bucket said, pausing to think about it, "no . . . I'm not so sure that I should."

"But you *must*."

"There's no *must* about it, my dear," Mr. Bucket said gently. "Mind you, I'd *love* to go. It'll be tremendously exciting. But on the other hand . . . I believe that the person who really *deserves* to go most of all is Grandpa Joe himself. He seems to know more about it than we do. Provided, of course, that he feels well enough. . . ."

"Yippeeeeee!" shouted Grandpa Joe, seizing Charlie by the hands and dancing round the room.

"He certainly *seems* well enough," Mrs. Bucket said, laughing. "Yes . . . perhaps you're right after all. Perhaps

Grandpa Joe should be the one to go with him. I certainly can't go myself and leave the other three old people all alone in bed for a whole day."

"Hallelujah!" yelled Grandpa Joe. "Praise the Lord!"

At that point, there came a loud knock on the front door. Mr. Bucket went to open it, and the next moment, swarms of newspapermen and photographers were pouring into the house. They had tracked down the finder of the fifth Golden Ticket, and now they all wanted to get the full story for the front pages of morning papers. For several hours, there was complete pandemonium in the little house, and it must have been nearly midnight before Mr. Bucket was able to get rid of them so that Charlie could go to bed.

13
The Big Day Arrives

THE SUN WAS SHINING BRIGHTLY on the morning of the big day, but the ground was still white with snow and the air was very cold.

Outside the gates of Wonka's factory, enormous crowds of people had gathered to watch the five lucky ticket holders going in. The excitement was tremendous. It was just before ten o'clock. The crowds were pushing and shouting, and policemen with arms linked were trying to hold them back from the gates.

Right beside the gates, in a small group that was carefully shielded from the crowds by the police, stood the five famous children, together with the grownups who had come with them.

The tall bony old figure of Grandpa Joe could be seen standing quietly among them, and beside him, holding tightly on to his hand, was little Charlie Bucket himself.

All the children, except Charlie, had both their mothers and fathers with them, and it was a good thing that they had, otherwise the whole party might have gotten out of hand. They were so eager to get going that their parents were having to hold them back by force to prevent them from climbing over the gates. "Be patient!" cried the fathers. "Be still! It's not *time* yet! It's not ten o'clock!"

Behind him, Charlie Bucket could hear the shouts of the people in the crowd as they pushed and fought to get a glimpse of the famous children.

"There's Violet Beauregarde!" he heard someone shouting. "That's her all right! I can remember her face from the newspapers!"

"And you know what?" somebody else shouted back. "She's still chewing that dreadful old piece of gum she's had for three months! You look at her jaws! They're still working on it!"

"Who's the big fat boy?"

"That's Augustus Gloop!"

"So it is!"

"Enormous, isn't he!"

"Fantastic!"

"Who's the kid with a picture of The Lone Ranger stenciled on his windbreaker?"

"That's Mike Teavee! He's the television fiend!"

"He must be crazy! Look at all those crazy pistols he's got hanging all over him!"

"The one *I* want to see is Veruca Salt!" shouted another voice in the crowd. "She's the girl whose father bought up half a million candy bars and then made the workers in his peanut factory unwrap every one of them until they found a Golden Ticket! He gives her anything she wants! Absolutely anything! She only has to start screaming for it and she gets it!"

"Dreadful, isn't it?"

"Shocking, I call it!"

"Which do you think is her?"

"That one! Over there on the left! The little girl in the silver mink coat!"

"Which one is Charlie Bucket?"

"Charlie Bucket? He must be that skinny little shrimp standing beside the old fellow who looks like a skeleton. Right close to us. Just there! See him?"

"Why hasn't he got a coat on in this cold weather?"

"Don't ask me. Maybe he can't afford to buy one."

"Jeepers! He must be freezing!"

Charlie, standing only a few paces away from the speaker, gave Grandpa Joe's hand a squeeze, and the old man looked down at Charlie and smiled.

Somewhere in the distance, a church clock began striking ten.

Very slowly, with a loud creaking of rusty hinges, the

great iron gates of the factory began to swing open.

The crowd became suddenly silent. The children stopped jumping about. All eyes were fixed upon the gates.

"There he is!" somebody shouted. *"That's him!"*

And so it was!

14
Mr. Willy Wonka

MR. WONKA WAS STANDING all alone just inside the open gates of the factory.

And what an extraordinary little man he was!

He had a black top hat on his head.

He wore a tail coat made of a beautiful plum-colored velvet.

His trousers were bottle green.

His gloves were pearly gray.

And in one hand he carried a fine gold-topped walking cane.

Covering his chin, there was a small neat pointed black beard—a goatee. And his eyes—his eyes were most marvelously bright. They seemed to be sparkling and twinkling at you all the time. The whole face, in fact, was alight with fun and laughter.

And oh, how clever he looked! How quick and sharp and full of life! He kept making quick jerky little movements with his head, cocking it this way and that, and taking everything in with those bright twinkling eyes. He was like a squirrel in the quickness of his movements, like a quick clever old squirrel from the park.

Suddenly, he did a funny little skipping dance in the snow, and he spread his arms wide, and he smiled at the five children who were clustered near the gates, and he called out, "Welcome, my little friends! Welcome to the factory!"

His voice was high and flutey. "Will you come forward one at a time, please," he called out, "and bring your parents. Then show me your Golden Ticket and give me your name. Who's first?"

The big fat boy stepped up. "I'm Augustus Gloop," he said.

"Augustus!" cried Mr. Wonka, seizing his hand and pumping it up and down with terrific force. "My *dear* boy, how *good* to see you! Delighted! Charmed! Overjoyed to have you with us! And *these* are your parents? How nice! Come in! Come in! That's right! Step through the gates!"

Mr. Wonka was clearly just as excited as everybody else.

"My name," said the next child to go forward, "is Veruca Salt."

"My *dear* Veruca! How *do* you do? What a pleasure this is! You *do* have an interesting name, don't you? I always thought that a veruca was a sort of wart that you got on the sole of your foot! But I must be wrong, mustn't I? How pretty you look in that lovely mink coat! I'm so glad you could come! Dear me, this is going to be *such* an exciting day! I *do* hope you enjoy it! I'm sure you *will*! I *know* you will! Your father? How *are* you, Mr. Salt? And Mrs. Salt? Overjoyed to see you! Yes, the ticket is *quite* in order! Please go in!"

The next two children, Violet Beauregarde and Mike Teavee, came forward to have their tickets examined and then to have their arms practically pumped off their shoulders by the energetic Mr. Wonka.

And last of all, a small nervous voice whispered, "Charlie Bucket."

"Charlie!" cried Mr. Wonka. "Well, well, well! So *there*

you are! You're the one who found your ticket only yesterday, aren't you? Yes, yes. I read *all* about it in this morning's papers! *Just* in time, my dear boy! I'm so glad! So happy for you! And this? Your grandfather? Delighted to meet you, sir! Overjoyed! Enraptured! Enchanted! All right! Excellent! Is everybody in now? Five children? Yes! Good! Now will you please follow me! Our tour is about to begin! But *do* keep together! *Please* don't wander off by yourselves! I shouldn't like to lose any of you at *this* stage of the proceedings! Oh, dear me, no!"

Charlie glanced back over his shoulder and saw the great iron entrance gates slowly closing behind him. The crowds on the outside were still pushing and shouting. Charlie took a last look at them. Then, as the gates closed with a clang, all sight of the outside world disappeared.

"Here we are!" cried Mr. Wonka, trotting along in front of the group. "Through this big red door, please! *That's* right! It's nice and warm inside! I have to keep it warm inside the factory because of the workers! My workers are used to an *extremely* hot climate! They can't stand the cold! They'd perish if they went outdoors in this weather! They'd freeze to death!"

"But who *are* these workers?" asked Augustus Gloop.

"All in good time, my dear boy!" said Mr. Wonka, smiling at Augustus. "Be patient! You shall see everything as we go along! Are all of you inside? Good! Would you mind closing the door? Thank you."

Charlie Bucket found himself standing in a long corridor that stretched away in front of him as far as he could see. The corridor was so wide that a car could easily have been driven along it. The walls were pale pink, the lighting was soft and pleasant.

"How lovely and warm!" whispered Charlie.

"I know. And what a marvelous smell!" answered Grandpa Joe, taking a long deep sniff. All the most wonderful smells in the world seemed to be mixed up in the air around them—the smell of roasting coffee and burnt sugar and melting chocolate and mint and violets and crushed hazelnuts and apple blossom and caramel and lemon peel. . . .

And far away in the distance, from the heart of the great factory, came a muffled roar of energy as though some monstrous gigantic machine were spinning its wheels at breakneck speed.

"Now *this,* my dear children," said Mr. Wonka, raising his voice above the noise, "this is the main corridor. Will you please hang your coats and hats on those pegs over there, and then follow me. *That's* the way! Good! Everyone ready! Come on, then! Here we go!" He trotted off rapidly down the corridor with the tails of his plum-colored velvet coat flapping behind him, and the visitors all hurried after him.

It was quite a large party of people, when you came to think of it. There were nine grownups and five children, fourteen in all. So you can imagine that there was a good deal of pushing and shoving as they hustled and bustled down the passage, trying to keep up with the swift little figure in front of them. "Come *on!*" cried Mr. Wonka. "Get a move on, please! We'll *never* get round today if you dawdle like this!"

Soon, he turned right off the main corridor into another slightly narrower passage.

Then he turned left.

Then left again.

Then right.

Then left.

Then right.

Then right.

Then left.

The place was like a gigantic rabbit warren, with passages leading this way and that in every direction.

"Don't you let go my hand, Charlie," whispered Grandpa Joe.

"Notice how all these passages are sloping downwards!" called Mr. Wonka. "We are now going underground! *All* the most important rooms in my factory are deep down below the surface!"

"Why is that?" somebody asked.

"There wouldn't be *nearly* enough space for them up on top!" answered Mr. Wonka. "These rooms we are going to see are *enormous*! They're larger than football fields! No building in the *world* would be big enough to house them! But down here, underneath the ground, I've got *all* the space I want. There's no limit—so long as I hollow it out."

Mr. Wonka turned right.

He turned left.

He turned right again.

The passages were sloping steeper and steeper downhill now.

Then suddenly, Mr. Wonka stopped. In front of him, there was a shiny metal door. The party crowded round. On the door, in large letters, it said:

THE CHOCOLATE ROOM

15

The Chocolate Room

"AN IMPORTANT ROOM, THIS!" cried Mr. Wonka, taking a bunch of keys from his pocket and slipping one into the keyhole of the door. "*This* is the nerve center of the whole factory, the heart of the whole business! And so *beautiful*! I *insist* upon my rooms being beautiful! I can't *abide* ugliness in factories! *In* we go, then! But *do* be careful, my dear children! Don't lose your heads! Don't get overexcited! Keep very calm!"

Mr. Wonka opened the door. Five children and nine grownups pushed their ways in—and *oh,* what an amazing sight it was that now met their eyes!

They were looking down upon a lovely valley. There were green meadows on either side of the valley, and along the bottom of it there flowed a great brown river.

What is more, there was a tremendous waterfall halfway along the river—a steep cliff over which the water curled and rolled in a solid sheet, and then went crashing down into a boiling churning whirlpool of froth and spray.

Below the waterfall (and this was the most astonishing sight of all), a whole mass of enormous glass pipes were dangling down into the river from somewhere high up in the ceiling! They really were *enormous,* those pipes. There must have been a dozen of them at least, and they were sucking up the brownish muddy water from the river and carrying it away to goodness knows where. And because they were made of glass, you could see the liquid flowing and bubbling along inside them, and above the noise of the waterfall, you could hear the never-ending suck-suck-sucking sound of the pipes as they did their work.

Graceful trees and bushes were growing along the riverbanks—weeping willows and alders and tall clumps of rhododendrons with their pink and red and mauve blossoms. In the meadows there were thousands of buttercups.

"There!" cried Mr. Wonka, dancing up and down and pointing his gold-topped cane at the great brown river. "It's *all* chocolate! Every drop of that river is hot melted chocolate of the finest quality. The *very* finest quality. There's enough chocolate in there to fill *every* bathtub in the *entire* country! *And* all the swimming pools as well! Isn't it *terrific*? And just look at my pipes! They suck up the chocolate and carry it away to all the other rooms in the factory where it is needed! Thousands of gallons an hour, my dear children! Thousands and thousands of gallons!"

The children and their parents were too flabbergasted to speak. They were staggered. They were dumfounded. They were bewildered and dazzled. They were com-

pletely bowled over by the hugeness of the whole thing. They simply stood and stared.

"The waterfall is *most* important!" Mr. Wonka went on. "It mixes the chocolate! It churns it up! It pounds it and beats it! It makes it light and frothy! No other factory in the world mixes its chocolate by waterfall! But it's the *only* way to do it properly! The *only* way! And do you like my trees?" he cried, pointing with his stick. "And my lovely bushes? Don't you think they look pretty? I told you I hated ugliness! And of course they are *all* eatable! All made of something different and delicious! And do you like my meadows? Do you like my grass and my buttercups? The grass you are standing on, my dear little ones, is made of a new kind of soft, minty sugar that I've just invented! I call it swudge! Try a blade! Please do! It's delectable!"

Automatically, everybody bent down and picked one blade of grass—everybody, that is, except Augustus Gloop, who took a big handful.

And Violet Beauregarde, before tasting her blade of grass, took the piece of world-record-breaking chewing gum out of her mouth and stuck it carefully behind her ear.

"Isn't it *wonderful*!" whispered Charlie. "Hasn't it got a wonderful taste, Grandpa?"

"I could eat the whole *field*!" said Grandpa Joe, grinning with delight. "I could go around on all fours like a cow and eat every blade of grass in the field!"

"Try a buttercup!" cried Mr. Wonka. "They're even *nicer*!"

Suddenly, the air was filled with screams of excitement. The screams came from Veruca Salt. She was point-ing frantically to the other side of the river. "*Look*! Look over there!" she screamed. "What *is* it? He's moving! He's walking! It's a little *person*! It's a little *man*! Down there below the waterfall!"

Everybody stopped picking buttercups and stared across the river.

"She's right, Grandpa!" cried Charlie. "It *is* a little man! Can you *see* him?"

"I see him, Charlie!" said Grandpa Joe excitedly.

And now everybody started shouting at once.

"There's *two* of them!"

"My gosh, so there is!"

"There's more than two! There's one, two, three, four, five!"

"What are they *doing*?"

"Where do they *come* from?"

"Who *are* they?"

Children and parents alike rushed down to the edge of the river to get a closer look.

"Aren't they *fantastic*!"

"No higher than my knee!"

"Look at their funny long hair!"

The tiny men—they were no larger than medium-sized dolls—had stopped what they were doing, and now they were staring back across the river at the visitors. One of them pointed towards the children, and then he whispered something to the other four, and all five of them burst into peals of laughter.

"But they can't be *real* people," Charlie said.

"Of course they're real people," Mr. Wonka answered. "They're Oompa-Loompas."

16
The Oompa-Loompas

"OOMPA-LOOMPAS!" everyone said at once. *"Oompa-Loompas!"*

"Imported direct from Loompaland," said Mr. Wonka proudly.

"There's no such place," said Mrs. Salt.

"Excuse me, dear lady, but . . ."

"Mr. Wonka," cried Mrs. Salt. "I am a teacher of geography . . ."

"Then you'll know all about it," said Mr. Wonka. "And oh, what a terrible country it is! Nothing but thick jungles infested by the most dangerous beasts in the entire world—hornswogglers and snozzwangers and those terrible wicked whangdoodles. A whangdoodle would eat ten Oompa-Loompas for breakfast and come galloping back for a second helping. When I went out there, I found the little Oompa-Loompas living in tree-houses. They *had* to live in tree-houses to escape from the whangdoodles and the hornswogglers and the snozzwangers. And they were practically starving to death. They were living on green caterpillars, and the caterpillars tasted revolting, and the Oompa-Loompas spent every moment of their days climbing through the treetops looking for other things to mash up with the caterpillars to make them taste better—red beetles, for instance, and eucalyptus leaves, and the bark of the bong-bong tree, all of them beastly, but not quite so beastly as the caterpillars. Poor little Oompa-Loompas! The one food that they longed for more than any other was the cacao bean. But they couldn't get it. An Oompa-Loompa was lucky if he found three or four cacao beans a year. But oh, how they craved them. They used to dream about cacao beans all night and talk about them all day. You had only to *mention* the word 'cacao' to an Oompa-Loompa and he would start dribbling at the mouth. The cacao bean," Mr. Wonka continued, "which grows on the cacao tree, happens to be *the thing* from which all chocolate is made. You cannot make chocolate without the cacao bean. The cacao bean *is* chocolate. I myself use billions of cacao beans every week in this factory. And so, my dear children, as soon as

I discovered that the Oompa-Loompas were crazy for this particular food, I climbed up to their tree-house village and poked my head in through the door of the tree house belonging to the leader of the tribe. The poor little fellow, looking thin and starved, was sitting there trying to eat a bowl full of mashed-up green caterpillars without being sick. 'Look here,' I said (speaking not in English, of course, but in Oompa-Loompish), 'look here, if you and all your people will come back to my country and live in my factory, you can have *all* the cacao beans you want! I've got mountains of them in my storehouses! You can have cacao beans for every meal! You can gorge yourselves silly on them! I'll even pay your wages in cacao beans if you wish!'

"'You really mean it?' asked the Oompa-Loompa leader, leaping up from his chair.

"'Of course I mean it,' I said. 'And you can have chocolate as well. Chocolate tastes even better than cacao beans because it's got milk and sugar added.'

"The little man gave a great whoop of joy and threw his bowl of mashed caterpillars right out of the treehouse window. 'It's a deal!' he cried. 'Come on! Let's go!'

"So I shipped them all over here, every man, woman, and child in the Oompa-Loompa tribe. It was easy. I smuggled them over in large packing cases with holes in them, and they all got here safely. They are wonderful workers. They all speak English now. They love dancing and music. They are always making up songs. I expect you will hear a good deal of singing today from time to time. I must warn you, though, that they are rather mischievous. They like jokes. They still wear the same kind of clothes they wore in the jungle. They insist upon that. The men, as you can see for yourselves across the river, wear only deerskins. The women wear leaves, and the children wear nothing at all. The women use fresh leaves every day. . . ."

"Daddy!" shouted Veruca Salt (the girl who got everything she wanted). *"Daddy!* I want an Oompa-Loompa! I want you to get me an Oompa-Loompa! I want an Oompa-Loompa right away! I want to take it home with me! Go on, Daddy! Get me an Oompa-Loompa!"

"Now, now, my pet!" her father said to her, "we mustn't interrupt Mr. Wonka."

"But I want an Oompa-Loompa!" screamed Veruca.

"All *right,* Veruca, all *right.* But I can't get it for you this second. Please be patient. I'll see you have one before the day is out."

"Augustus!" shouted Mrs. Gloop. "Augustus, sweetheart,

I don't think you had better do *that*." Augustus Gloop, as you might have guessed, had quietly sneaked down to the edge of the river, and he was now kneeling on the river-bank, scooping hot melted chocolate into his mouth as fast as he could.

17
Augustus Gloop Goes up the Pipe

WHEN MR. WONKA turned round and saw what Augustus Gloop was doing, he cried out, "Oh, no! *Please*, Augustus, *please*! I beg of you not to do that. My chocolate must be untouched by human hands!"

"Augustus!" called out Mrs. Gloop. "Didn't you hear what the man said? Come away from that river at once!"

"This stuff is *tee*-riffic!" said Augustus, taking not the slightest notice of his mother or Mr. Wonka. "Oh boy, I need a bucket to drink it properly!"

"Augustus," cried Mr. Wonka, hopping up and down and waggling his stick in the air, "you *must* come away. You are dirtying my chocolate!"

"Augustus!" cried Mrs. Gloop.

"Augustus!" cried Mr. Gloop.

But Augustus was deaf to everything except the call of his enormous stomach. He was now lying full length on the ground with his head far out over the river, lapping up the chocolate like a dog.

"Augustus!" shouted Mrs. Gloop. "You'll be giving that nasty cold of yours to about a million people all over the country!"

"Be careful, Augustus!" shouted Mr. Gloop. "You're leaning too far out!"

Mr. Gloop was absolutely right. For suddenly there was a shriek, and then a splash, and into the river went Augustus Gloop, and in one second he had disappeared under the brown surface.

"Save him!" screamed Mrs. Gloop, going white in the face, and waving her umbrella about. "He'll drown! He can't swim a yard! Save him! Save him!"

"Good heavens, woman," said Mr. Gloop, "I'm not diving in there! I've got my best suit on!"

Augustus Gloop's face came up again to the surface, painted brown with chocolate. "Help! Help! Help!" he yelled. "Fish me out!"

"Don't just *stand* there!" Mrs. Gloop screamed at Mr. Gloop. "*Do* something!"

"I *am* doing something!" said Mr. Gloop, who was now taking off his jacket and getting ready to dive into the chocolate. But while he was doing this, the wretched boy was being sucked closer and closer toward the mouth of one of the great pipes that was dangling down into the river. Then all at once, the powerful suction took hold of him completely, and he was pulled under the surface and then into the mouth of the pipe.

The crowd on the riverbank waited breathlessly to see where he would come out.

"There he goes!" somebody shouted, pointing upwards.

And sure enough, because the pipe was made of glass, Augustus Gloop could be clearly seen shooting up inside it, head first, like a torpedo.

"Help! Murder! Police!" screamed Mrs. Gloop. "Augustus, come back at once! Where are you going?"

"It's a wonder to me," said Mr. Gloop, "how that pipe is big enough for him to go through it."

"It *isn't* big enough!" said Charlie Bucket. "Oh dear, look! He's slowing down!"

"So he is!" said Grandpa Joe.

"He's going to stick!" said Charlie.

"I think he is!" said Grandpa Joe.

"By golly, he *has* stuck!" said Charlie.

"It's his stomach that's done it!" said Mr. Gloop.

"He's blocked the whole pipe!" said Grandpa Joe.

"Smash the pipe!" yelled Mrs. Gloop, still waving her umbrella. "Augustus, come out of there at once!"

The watchers below could see the chocolate swishing around the boy in the pipe, and they could see it building up behind him in a solid mass, pushing against the blockage. The pressure was terrific. Something had to give. Something did give, and that something was Augustus. *whoof!* Up he shot again like a bullet in the barrel of a gun.

"He's disappeared!" yelled Mrs. Gloop. "Where does that pipe go to? Quick! Call the fire brigade!"

"Keep calm!" cried Mr. Wonka. "Keep calm, my dear lady, keep calm. There is no danger! No danger whatsoever! Augustus has gone on a little journey, that's all. A most interesting little journey. But he'll come out of it just fine, you wait and see."

"How can he possibly come out just fine!" snapped Mrs. Gloop. "He'll be made into marshmallows in five seconds!"

"Impossible!" cried Mr. Wonka. "Unthinkable! Inconceivable! Absurd! He could never be made into marshmallows!"

"And why not, may I ask?" shouted Mrs. Gloop.

"Because that pipe doesn't *go* to the Marshmallow Room!" Mr. Wonka answered. "It doesn't go anywhere near it! That pipe—the one Augustus went up—happens to lead directly to the room where I make a most delicious kind of strawberry-flavored chocolate-coated fudge. . . ."

"Then he'll be made into strawberry-flavored chocolate-coated fudge!" screamed Mrs. Gloop. "My poor Augustus! They'll be selling him by the pound all over the country tomorrow morning!"

"Quite right," said Mr. Gloop.

"I *know* I'm right," said Mrs. Gloop.

"It's beyond a joke," said Mr. Gloop.

"Mr. Wonka doesn't seem to think so!" cried Mrs. Gloop. "Just look at him! He's laughing his head off! How *dare* you laugh like that when my boy's just gone up the pipe! You monster!" she shrieked, pointing her umbrella at Mr. Wonka as though she were going to run him through. "You think it's a joke, do you? You think that sucking my boy up into your Fudge Room like that is just one great big colossal joke?"

"He'll be perfectly safe," said Mr. Wonka, giggling slightly.

"He'll be chocolate fudge!" shrieked Mrs. Gloop.

"Never!" cried Mr. Wonka.

"Of course he will!" shrieked Mrs. Gloop.

"I wouldn't allow it!" cried Mr. Wonka.

"And why not?" shrieked Mrs. Gloop.

"Because the taste would be terrible," said Mr. Wonka. "Just imagine it! Augustus-flavored chocolate-coated Gloop! No one would buy it."

"They most certainly would!" cried Mr. Gloop indignantly.

"I don't want to think about it!" shrieked Mrs. Gloop.

"Nor do I," said Mr. Wonka. "And I do promise you, madam, that your darling boy is perfectly safe."

"If he's perfectly safe, then where is he?" snapped Mrs. Gloop. "Lead me to him this instant!"

Mr. Wonka turned around and clicked his fingers sharply, *click, click, click,* three times. Immediately, an Oompa-Loompa appeared, as if from nowhere, and stood beside him.

The Oompa-Loompa bowed and smiled, showing beautiful white teeth. His skin was rosy-white, his long hair was golden-brown, and the top of his head came just above the height of Mr. Wonka's knee. He wore the usual deerskin slung over his shoulder.

"Now listen to me!" said Mr. Wonka, looking down at the tiny man, "I want you to take Mr. and Mrs. Gloop up to the Fudge Room and help them to find their son, Augustus. He's just gone up the pipe."

The Oompa-Loompa took one look at Mrs. Gloop and exploded into peals of laughter.

"Oh, do be quiet!" said Mr. Wonka. "Control yourself! Pull yourself together! Mrs. Gloop doesn't think it's at all funny!"

"You can say that again!" said Mrs. Gloop.

"Go straight to the Fudge Room," Mr. Wonka said to the Oompa-Loompa, "and when you get there, take a long stick and start poking around inside the big chocolate-mixing barrel. I'm almost certain you'll find him in there.

But you'd better look sharp! You'll have to hurry! If you leave him in the chocolate-mixing barrel too long, he's liable to get poured out into the fudge boiler, and that really *would* be a disaster, wouldn't it? My fudge would become *quite* uneatable!"

Mrs. Gloop let out a shriek of fury.

"I'm joking," said Mr. Wonka, giggling madly behind his beard. "I didn't mean it. Forgive me. I'm so sorry. Good-by, Mrs. Gloop! And Mr. Gloop! Good-by! Good-by! I'll see you later. . . ."

As Mr. and Mrs. Gloop and their tiny escort hurried away, the five Oompa-Loompas on the far side of the river suddenly began hopping and dancing about and beating wildly upon a number of very small drums. "Augustus Gloop!" they chanted. "Augustus Gloop! Augustus Gloop! Augustus Gloop!"

"Grandpa!" cried Charlie. "Listen to them, Grandpa! What *are* they doing?"

"Ssshh!" whispered Grandpa Joe. "I think they're going to sing us a song!"

"Augustus Gloop!" chanted the Oompa-Loompas.
"Augustus Gloop! Augustus Gloop!
The great big greedy nincompoop!
How long could we allow this beast
To gorge and guzzle, feed and feast
On everything he wanted to?
Great Scott! It simply wouldn't do!
However long this pig might live,
We're positive he'd never give
Even the smallest bit of fun

Or happiness to anyone.
So what we do in cases such
As this, we use the gentle touch,
And carefully we take the brat
And turn him into something that
Will give great pleasure to us all—
A doll, for instance, or a ball,
Or marbles or a rocking horse.
But this revolting boy, of course,
Was so unutterably vile,
So greedy, foul, and infantile,
He left a most disgusting taste
Inside our mouths, and so in haste
We chose a thing that, come what may,
Would take the nasty taste away.
'Come on!' we cried, 'The time is ripe
To send him shooting up the pipe!
He has to go! It has to be!'
And very soon, he's going to see
Inside the room to which he's gone
Some funny things are going on.
But don't, dear children, be alarmed;
Augustus Gloop will not be harmed,
Although, of course, we must admit
He will be altered *quite a bit.*
He'll be quite *changed from what he's been,*
When he goes through the fudge machine:
Slowly, the wheels go round and round,
The cogs begin to grind and pound;
A hundred knives to slice, slice, slice;
We add some sugar, cream, and spice;

We boil him for a minute more,
Until we're absolutely sure
That all the greed and all the gall
Is boiled away for once and all.
Then out he comes! And now! By grace!
A miracle has taken place!
This boy, who only just before
Was loathed by men from shore to shore,
This greedy brute, this louse's ear,
Is loved by people everywhere!
For who could hate or bear a grudge
Against a luscious bit of fudge?"

"I *told* you they loved singing!" cried Mr. Wonka. "Aren't they delightful? Aren't they charming? But you mustn't believe a word they said. It's all nonsense, every bit of it!"

"Are the Oompa-Loompas really joking, Grandpa?" asked Charlie.

"Of course they're joking," answered Grandpa Joe. "They *must* be joking. At least, I hope they're joking. Don't you?"

18
Down the Chocolate River

"OFF WE GO!" cried Mr. Wonka. "Hurry up, everybody! Follow me to the next room! And please don't worry about

Augustus Gloop. He's bound to come out in the wash. They always do. We shall have to make the next part of the journey by boat! Here she comes! Look!"

A steamy mist was rising up now from the great warm chocolate river, and out of the mist there appeared suddenly a most fantastic pink boat. It was a large open rowboat with a tall front and a tall back (like a Viking boat of old), and it was of such a shining sparkling glistening pink color that the whole thing looked as though it were made of bright, pink glass. There were many oars on either side of it, and as the boat came closer, the watchers on the riverbank could see that the oars were being pulled by masses of Oompa-Loompas—at least ten of them to each oar.

"This is my private yacht!" cried Mr. Wonka, beaming with pleasure. "I made her by hollowing out an enormous boiled sweet! Isn't she beautiful! See how she comes cutting through the river!"

The gleaming pink boiled-sweet boat glided up to the riverbank. One hundred Oompa-Loompas rested on their oars and stared up at the visitors. Then suddenly, for some reason best known to themselves, they all burst into shrieks of laughter.

"What's so funny?" asked Violet Beauregarde.

"Oh, don't worry about *them*!" cried Mr. Wonka. "They're always laughing! They think everything's a colossal joke! Jump into the boat, all of you! Come on! Hurry up!"

As soon as everyone was safely in, the Oompa-Loompas pushed the boat away from the bank and began to row swiftly down river.

"Hey, there! Mike Teavee!" shouted Mr. Wonka. "Please

do not lick the boat with your tongue! It'll only make it sticky!"

"Daddy," said Veruca Salt, "I want a boat like this! I want you to buy me a big pink boiled-sweet boat exactly like Mr. Wonka's! And I want lots of Oompa-Loompas to row me about, and I want a chocolate river and I want . . . I want . . ."

"She wants a good kick in the pants," whispered Grandpa Joe to Charlie. The old man was sitting in the back of the boat and little Charlie Bucket was right beside him. Charlie was holding tightly onto his grandfather's bony old hand. He was in a whirl of excitement. Everything that he had seen so far—the great chocolate river, the waterfall, the huge sucking pipes, the candy meadows, the Oompa-Loompas, the beautiful pink boat, and most of all, Mr. Willy Wonka himself—had been so astonishing that he began to wonder whether there could possibly be any more astonishments left. Where were they going now? What were they going to see? And what in the world was going to happen in the next room?

"Isn't it marvelous?" said Grandpa Joe, grinning at Charlie.

Charlie nodded and smiled up at the old man.

Suddenly, Mr. Wonka, who was sitting on Charlie's other side, reached down into the bottom of the boat, picked up a large mug, dipped it into the river, filled it with chocolate, and handed it to Charlie. "Drink this," he said. "It'll do you good! You looked starved to death!"

Then Mr. Wonka filled a second mug and gave it to Grandpa Joe. "You, too," he said. "You look like a skeleton! What's the matter? Hasn't there been anything to eat in your house lately?"

"Not much," said Grandpa Joe.

Charlie put the mug to his lips, and as the rich warm creamy chocolate ran down his throat into his empty tummy, his whole body from head to toe began to tingle with pleasure, and a feeling of intense happiness spread over him.

"You like it?" asked Mr. Wonka.

"Oh, it's wonderful!" Charlie said.

"The creamiest loveliest chocolate I've ever tasted!" said Grandpa Joe, smacking his lips.

"That's because it's been mixed by waterfall," Mr. Wonka told him.

The boat sped on down the river. The river was getting narrower. There was some kind of a dark tunnel ahead—a great round tunnel that looked like an enormous pipe—and the river was running right into the tunnel. And so was the boat! "Row on!" shouted Mr. Wonka, jumping up and waving his stick in the air. "Full speed ahead!" And with the Oompa-Loompas rowing faster than ever, the boat shot into the pitch-dark tunnel, and all the passengers screamed with excitement.

"How can they see where they're going?" shrieked Violet Beauregarde in the darkness.

"There's no knowing where they're going!" cried Mr. Wonka, hooting with laughter.

> *"There's no earthly way of knowing*
> *Which direction they are going!*
> *There's no knowing where they're rowing,*
> *Or which way the river's flowing!*
> *Not a speck of light is showing,*

So the danger must be growing,
For the rowers keep on rowing,
And they're certainly not showing
Any signs that they are slowing...."

"He's gone off his rocker!" shouted one of the fathers, aghast, and the other parents joined in the chorus of frightened shouting. "He's crazy!" they shouted.

"He's balmy!"

"He's nutty!"

"He's screwy!"

"He's batty!"

"He's dippy!"

"He's dotty!"

"He's daffy!"

"He's goofy!"

"He's beany!"

"He's buggy!"

"He's wacky!"

"He's loony!"

"No, he is *not*!" said Grandpa Joe.

"Switch on the lights!" shouted Mr. Wonka. And suddenly, on came the lights and the whole tunnel was brilliantly lit up, and Charlie could see that they were indeed inside a gigantic pipe, and the great upward-curving walls of the pipe were pure white and spotlessly clean. The river of chocolate was flowing very fast inside the pipe, and the Oompa-Loompas were all rowing like crazy, and the boat was rocketing along at a furious pace. Mr. Wonka was jumping up and down in the back of the boat and calling to the rowers to row faster and faster still. He seemed to love the sensation of whizzing through a white tunnel in a pink boat on a chocolate river, and he clapped his hands and laughed and kept glancing at his passengers to see if they were enjoying it as much as he.

"Look, Grandpa!" cried Charlie. "There's a door in the wall!" It was a green door and it was set into the wall of the tunnel just above the level of the river. As they flashed past it there was just enough time to read the writing on the door: STOREROOM NUMBER 54, it said. ALL THE CREAMS—DAIRY CREAM, WHIPPED CREAM, VIOLET CREAM, COFFEE CREAM, PINEAPPLE CREAM, VANILLA CREAM, AND HAIR CREAM.

"Hair cream?" cried Mike Teavee. "You don't use *hair cream*?"

"Row on!" shouted Mr. Wonka. "There's no time to answer silly questions!"

They streaked past a black door. STOREROOM NUMBER 71, it said on it. WHIPS—ALL SHAPES AND SIZES.

"*Whips!*" cried Veruca Salt. "What on earth do you use whips for?"

"For whipping cream, of course," said Mr. Wonka. "How can you whip cream without whips? Whipped cream isn't whipped cream at all unless it's been whipped with whips. Just as a poached egg isn't a poached egg unless it's been stolen from the woods in the dead of night! Row on, please!"

They passed a yellow door on which it said: STOREROOM NUMBER 77—ALL THE BEANS, CACAO BEANS, COFFEE BEANS, JELLY BEANS, AND HAS BEANS.

"*Has beans?*" cried Violet Beauregarde.

"You're one yourself!" said Mr. Wonka. "There's no time

for arguing! Press on, press on!" But five seconds later, when a bright red door came into sight ahead, he suddenly waved his gold-topped cane in the air and shouted, "Stop the boat!"

19

The Inventing Room—Everlasting Gobstoppers and Hair Toffee

WHEN MR. WONKA SHOUTED "Stop the boat!", the Oompa-Loompas jammed their oars into the river and backed water furiously. The boat stopped.

The Oompa-Loompas guided the boat alongside the red door. On the door it said, INVENTING ROOM—PRIVATE—KEEP OUT. Mr. Wonka took a key from his pocket, leaned over the side of the boat, and put the key in the keyhole.

"*This* is the most important room in the entire factory!" he said. "All my most secret new inventions are cooking and simmering in here! Old Fickelgruber would give his front teeth to be allowed inside just for three minutes! So would Prodnose and Slugworth and all the other rotten chocolate makers! But now, listen to me! I want no messing about when you go in! No touching, no meddling, and no tasting! Is that agreed?"

"Yes, yes!" the children cried. "We won't touch a thing!"

"Up to now," Mr. Wonka said, "nobody else, not even an

Oompa-Loompa, has ever been allowed in here!" He opened the door and stepped out of the boat into the room. The four children and their parents all scrambled after him.

"Don't touch!" shouted Mr. Wonka. "And don't knock anything over!"

Charlie Bucket started around the gigantic room in which he now found himself. The place was like a witch's kitchen! All about him black metal pots were boiling and bubbling on huge stoves, and kettles were hissing and pans were sizzling, and strange iron machines were clanking and spluttering, and there were pipes running all over the ceiling and walls, and the whole place was filled with smoke and steam and delicious rich smells.

Mr. Wonka himself had suddenly become even more excited than usual, and anyone could see that this was the room he loved best of all. He was hopping about among the saucepans and the machines like a child among his Christmas presents, not knowing which thing to look at first. He lifted the lid from a huge pot and took a sniff; then he rushed over and dipped a finger into a barrel of sticky yellow stuff and had a taste; then he skipped across to one of the machines and turned half a dozen knobs this way and that; then he peered anxiously through the glass door of a gigantic oven, rubbing his hands and cackling with delight at what he saw inside. Then he ran over to another machine, a small shiny affair that kept going *phut-phut-phut-phut-phut,* and every time it went *phut,* a large green marble dropped out of it into a basket on the floor. At least it looked like a marble.

"Everlasting Gobstoppers!" cried Mr. Wonka proudly.

"They're completely new! I am inventing them for children who are given very little pocket money. You can put an Everlasting Gobstopper in your mouth and you can suck it and suck it and suck it and suck it and suck it and it will *never* get any smaller!"

"It's like gum!" cried Violet Beauregarde.

"It is *not* like gum," Mr. Wonka said. "Gum is for chewing, and if you tried chewing one of these Gobstoppers here you'd break your teeth off. But they taste terrific! And they change color once a week! And they *never* get any smaller! They *never* disappear! *NEVER!* At least I don't think they do. There's one of them being tested this very moment in the Testing Room next door. An Oompa-Loompa is sucking it. He's been sucking it for very nearly a year now without stopping, and it's still just as good as ever!

"Now, over here," Mr. Wonka went on, skipping excitedly across the room to the opposite wall, "over here I am inventing a completely new line in toffees!" He stopped beside a large saucepan. The saucepan was full of thick gooey purplish treacle, boiling and bubbling. By standing on his toes, little Charlie could just see inside it.

"That's Hair Toffee!" cried Mr. Wonka. "You eat just one tiny bit of that, and in exactly half an hour a brand-new luscious thick silky beautiful crop of hair will start growing out all over the top of your head! And a moustache! And a beard!"

"A beard!" cried Veruca Salt. "Who wants a beard, for heaven's sake?"

"It would suit you very well," said Mr. Wonka, "but unfortunately the mixture is not quite right yet. I've got it too strong. It works too well. I tried it on an Oompa-

Loompa yesterday in the Testing Room and immediately a huge beard started shooting out of his chin, and the beard grew so fast that soon it was trailing all over the floor in a thick hairy carpet. It was growing faster than we could cut it! In the end we had to use a lawn mower to keep it in check! But I'll get the mixture right soon! And when I do, then there'll be no excuse any more for little boys and girls going about with bald heads!"

"But Mr. Wonka," said Mike Teavee, "little boys and girls never *do* go about with . . ."

"Don't argue, my dear child, *please* don't argue!" cried Mr. Wonka. "It's such a waste of precious time! Now, over *here*, if you will all step this way, I will show you something that I am terrifically proud of. Oh, do be careful! Don't knock anything over! Stand back!"

20
The Great Gum Machine

MR. WONKA LED THE PARTY over to a gigantic machine that stood in the very center of the Inventing Room. It was a mountain of gleaming metal that towered high above the children and their parents. Out of the very top of it there sprouted hundreds and hundreds of thin glass tubes, and the glass tubes all curled downwards and came together in a bunch and hung suspended over an enormous round tub as big as a bath.

"Here we go!" cried Mr. Wonka, and he pressed three different buttons on the side of the machine. A second later, a mighty rumbling sound came from inside it, and the whole machine began to shake most frighteningly, and steam began hissing out of it all over, and then suddenly the watchers noticed that runny stuff was pouring down the insides of all the hundreds of little glass tubes and squirting out into the great tub below. And in every single tube the runny stuff was of a different color, so that all the colors of the rainbow (and many others as well) came sloshing and splashing into the tub. It was a lovely sight. And when the tub was nearly full, Mr. Wonka pressed another button, and immediately the runny stuff stopped running out of the tubes, the rumbling sound disappeared, and a whizzing whirring noise took its place; and then a giant whizzer started whizzing round inside the enormous tub, mixing up all the different colored liquids like an ice-cream soda. Gradually, the mixture began to froth. It became frothier and frothier, and it turned from blue to white to green to brown to yellow, then back to blue again.

"Watch!" said Mr. Wonka.

Click went the machine, and the whizzer stopped whizzing. And now there came a sort of sucking noise, and very quickly all the blue frothy mixture in the huge basin was sucked back into the stomach of the machine. There was a moment of silence. Then a few queer rumblings were heard. Then silence again. Then suddenly, the machine let out a monstrous mighty groan, and at the same moment a tiny drawer (no bigger than the drawer in a slot machine) popped out of the side of the machine, and in the drawer there lay something so small and thin and grey that everyone thought it must be a mistake. The thing looked like a little strip of grey cardboard.

The children and their parents stared at the little grey strip lying in the drawer.

"You mean that's *all*?" said Mike Teavee, disgusted.

"That's all," answered Mr. Wonka, gazing proudly at the result. "Don't you know what it is?"

There was a pause. Then suddenly, Violet Beauregarde,

the goofy gum-chewing girl, let out a yell of excitement. "By gum, it's *gum*!" she shrieked. "It's a stick of chewing gum!"

"Right you are!" cried Mr. Wonka, slapping Violet hard on the back. "It's a stick of gum! It's a stick of the most *amazing* and *fabulous* and *sensational* gum in the world!"

21
Good-by Violet

"THIS GUM," Mr. Wonka went on, "is my latest, my greatest, my most fascinating invention! It's a chewing-gum meal! It's . . . it's . . . it's . . . that tiny little strip of gum lying there is a whole three-course dinner all by itself!"

"What sort of nonsense is this?" said one of the fathers.

"My dear sir!" cried Mr. Wonka, "when I start selling this gum in the shops it will change *everything*! It will be the end of all kitchens and all cooking! There will be no more marketing to do! No more buying of meat and groceries! There'll be no knives and forks at mealtimes! No plates! No washing up! No garbage! No mess! Just a little strip of Wonka's magic chewing gum—and that's all you'll ever need at breakfast, lunch, and supper! This piece of gum I've just made happens to be tomato soup, roast beef, and blueberry pie, but you can have almost anything you want!"

"What *do* you mean, it's tomato soup, roast beef, and blueberry pie?" said Violet Beauregarde.

"If you were to start chewing it," said Mr. Wonka, "then that is exactly what you would get on the menu. It's absolutely amazing! You can actually *feel* the food going down your throat and into your tummy! And you can taste it perfectly! And it fills you up! It satisfies you! It's terrific!"

"It's utterly impossible," said Veruca Salt.

"Just so long as it's gum," shouted Violet Beauregarde, "just so long as it's a piece of gum and I can chew it, then *that's* for me!" And quickly she took her own world-record piece of chewing gum out of her mouth and stuck it behind her left ear. "Come on, Mr. Wonka," she said, "hand over this magic gum of yours and we'll see if the thing works."

"Now, Violet," said Mrs. Beauregarde, her mother; "don't let's do anything silly, Violet."

"I want the gum!" Violet said obstinately. "What's so silly?"

"I would rather you didn't take it," Mr. Wonka told her gently. "You see, I haven't got it *quite right* yet. There are still one or two things. . . ."

"Oh, to heck with that!" said Violet, and suddenly, before Mr. Wonka could stop her, she shot out a fat hand and grabbed the stick of gum out of the little drawer and popped it into her mouth. At once, her huge well-trained jaws started chewing away on it like a pair of tongs.

"Don't!" said Mr. Wonka.

"Fabulous!" shouted Violet. "It's tomato soup! It's hot and creamy and delicious! I can feel it running down my throat!"

"Stop!" said Mr. Wonka. "The gum isn't ready yet! It's not right!"

"Of course it's right!" said Violet. "It's working beautifully! Oh my, what lovely soup this is!"

"Spit it out!" said Mr. Wonka.

"It's changing!" shouted Violet, chewing and grinning both at the same time. "The second course is coming up! It's roast beef! It's tender and juicy! Oh boy, what a flavor! The baked potato is marvelous, too! It's got a crispy skin and it's all filled with butter inside!"

"But how *in*-teresting, Violet," said Mrs. Beauregarde. "You *are* a clever girl."

"Keep chewing, kiddo!" said Mr. Beauregarde. "Keep right on chewing, baby! This is a great day for the Beauregardes! Our little girl is the first person in the world to have a chewing-gum meal!"

Everybody was watching Violet Beauregarde as she stood there chewing this extraordinary gum. Little Charlie Bucket was staring at her absolutely spellbound, watching her huge rubbery lips as they pressed and unpressed with the chewing, and Grandpa Joe stood beside him, gaping at the girl. Mr. Wonka was wringing his hands and saying, "No, no, no, no, no! It isn't ready for eating! It isn't right! You mustn't do it!"

"Blueberry pie and cream!" shouted Violet. "Here it comes! Oh my, it's perfect! It's beautiful! It's . . . it's exactly as though I'm swallowing it! It's as though I'm chewing and swallowing great big spoonfuls of the most marvelous blueberry pie in the world!"

"Good heavens, girl!" shrieked Mrs. Beauregarde suddenly, staring at Violet, "what's happening to your nose!"

"Oh, be quiet, mother, and let me finish!" said Violet.

"It's turning blue!" screamed Mrs. Beauregarde. "Your nose is turning blue as a blueberry!"

"Your mother is right!" shouted Mr. Beauregarde. "Your whole nose has gone purple!"

"What *do* you mean?" said Violet, still chewing away.

"Your cheeks!" screamed Mrs. Beauregarde. "They're turning blue as well! So is your chin! Your whole face is turning blue!"

"Spit that gum out at once!" ordered Mr. Beauregarde.

"Mercy! Save us!" yelled Mrs. Beauregarde. "The girl's going blue and purple all over! Even her hair is changing color! Violet, you're turning violet, Violet! What *is* happening to you!"

"I *told* you I hadn't got it quite right," sighed Mr. Wonka, shaking his head sadly.

"I'll say you haven't!" cried Mrs. Beauregarde. "Just look at the girl now!"

Everybody was staring at Violet. And what a terrible peculiar sight she was! Her face and hands and legs and neck, in fact the skin all over her body, as well as her great big mop of curly hair, had turned a brilliant, purplish-blue, the color of blueberry juice!

"It *always* goes wrong when we come to the dessert," sighed Mr. Wonka. "It's the blueberry pie that does it. But I'll get it right one day, you wait and see."

"Violet," screamed Mrs. Beauregarde, "you're swelling up!"

"I feel sick," Violet said.

"You're swelling up!" screamed Mrs. Beauregarde again.

"I feel most peculiar!" gasped Violet.

"I'm not surprised!" said Mr. Beauregarde.

"Great heavens, girl!" screeched Mrs. Beauregarde. "You're blowing up like a balloon!"

"Like a blueberry," said Mr. Wonka.

"Call a doctor!" shouted Mr. Beauregarde.

"Prick her with a pin!" said one of the other fathers.

"Save her!" cried Mrs. Beauregarde, wringing her hands.

But there was no saving her now. Her body was swelling up and changing shape at such a rate that within a minute it had turned into nothing less than an enormous round blue ball—a gigantic blueberry, in fact—and all that remained of Violet Beauregarde herself was a tiny pair of legs and a tiny pair of arms sticking out of the great round fruit and a little head on top.

"It *always* happens like that," sighed Mr. Wonka. "I've tried it twenty times in the Testing Room on twenty Oompa-Loompas, and every one of them finished up as a blueberry. It's most annoying. I just can't understand it."

"But I don't want a blueberry for a daughter!" yelled Mrs. Beauregarde. "Put her back to what she was this instant!"

Mr. Wonka clicked his fingers, and ten Oompa-Loompas appeared immediately at his side.

"Roll Miss Beauregarde into the boat," he said to them, "and take her along to the Juicing Room at once."

"The *Juicing Room*?" cried Mrs. Beauregarde. "What are they going to do to her there?"

"Squeeze her," said Mr. Wonka. "We've got to squeeze the juice out of her immediately. After that, we'll just have to see how she comes out. But don't worry, my dear Mrs. Beauregarde. We'll get her repaired if it's the last thing we do. I *am* sorry about it all, I really am. . . ."

Already the ten Oompa-Loompas were rolling the enormous blueberry across the floor of the Inventing Room toward the door that led to the chocolate river where the boat was waiting. Mr. and Mrs. Beauregarde hurried after them. The rest of the party, including little Charlie Bucket and Grandpa Joe, stood absolutely still and watched them go.

"Listen!" whispered Charlie. "Listen, Grandpa! The Oompa-Loompas in the boat outside are starting to sing!"

The voices, one hundred of them singing together, came loud and clear into the room:

> "*Dear friends, we surely all agree*
> *There's almost nothing worse to see*
> *Than some repulsive little bum*
> *Who's always chewing chewing gum.*
> *(It's very near as bad as those*

Who sit around and pick the nose).
So please believe us when we say
That chewing gum will never pay;
This sticky habit's bound to send
The chewer to a sticky end.
Did any of you ever know
A person called Miss Bigelow?
This dreadful woman saw no wrong
In chewing, chewing all day long.
She chewed while bathing in the tub,
She chewed while dancing at her club,
She chewed in church and on the bus;
It really was quite ludicrous!
And when she couldn't find her gum,
She'd chew up the linoleum,
Or anything that happened near—
A pair of boots, the postman's ear,
Or other people's underclothes,
And once she chewed her boy friend's nose.
She went on chewing till, at last,
Her chewing muscles grew so vast
That from her face her giant chin
Stuck out just like a violin.
For years and years she chewed away,
Consuming fifty packs a day,
Until one summer's eve, alas,
A horrid business came to pass.
Miss Bigelow went late to bed,
For half an hour she lay and read,
Chewing and chewing all the while
Like some great clockwork crocodile.

At last, she put her gum away
Upon a special little tray,
And settled back and went to sleep—
(She managed this by counting sheep).
But now, how strange! Although she slept,
Those massive jaws of hers still kept
On chewing, chewing through the night,
Even with nothing there to bite.
They were, you see, in such a groove
They positively had *to move.*
And very grim it was to hear
In pitch darkness, loud and clear,
This sleeping woman's great big trap
Opening and shutting, snap-snap-snap!
Faster and faster, chop-chop-chop,
The noise went on, it wouldn't stop.
Until at last her jaws decide

To pause and open extra wide,
And with the most tremendous chew
They bit the lady's tongue in two.
Thereafter, just from chewing gum,
Miss Bigelow was always dumb,
And spent her life shut up in some
Disgusting sanatorium.
And that is why we'll try so hard
To save Miss Violet Beauregarde
From suffering an equal fate.
She's still quite young. It's not too late,
Provided she survives the cure.
We hope she does. We can't be sure."

22
Along the Corridor

"WELL, WELL, WELL," sighed Mr. Willy Wonka, "two naughty little children gone. Three good little children left. I think we'd better get out of this room quickly before we lose anyone else!"

"But Mr. Wonka," said Charlie Bucket anxiously, "will Violet Beauregarde *ever* be all right again or will she always be a blueberry?"

"They'll de-juice her in no time flat!" declared Mr. Wonka. "They'll roll her into the de-juicing machine, and she'll come out just as thin as a whistle!"

"But will she still be blue all over?" asked Charlie.

"She'll be *purple!*" cried Mr. Wonka. "A fine rich purple from head to toe! But there you are! That's what comes from chewing disgusting gum all day long!"

"If you think gum is so disgusting," said Mike Teavee, "then why do you make it in your factory?"

"I do wish you wouldn't mumble," said Mr. Wonka. "I can't hear a word you're saying. Come on! Off we go! Hurry up! Follow me! We're going into the corridors again!" And so saying, Mr. Wonka scuttled across to the far end of the Inventing Room and went out through a small secret door hidden behind a lot of pipes and stoves. The three remaining children—Veruca Salt, Mike Teavee, and Charlie Bucket—together with the five remaining grown-ups, followed after him.

Charlie Bucket saw that they were now back in one of

those long pink corridors with many other pink corridors leading out of it. Mr. Wonka was rushing along in front, turning left and right and right and left, and Grandpa Joe was saying, "Keep a good hold of my hand, Charlie. It would be terrible to get lost in here."

Mr. Wonka was saying, "No time for any more messing about! We'll never get *anywhere* at the rate we've been going!" And on he rushed, down the endless pink corridors, with his black top hat perched on the top of his head and his plum-colored velvet coattails flying out behind him like a flag in the wind.

They passed another door, then another and another. There were doors every twenty paces or so along the corridor now, and they all had something written on them, and strange clanking noises were coming from behind several of them, and delicious smells came wafting through the keyholes, and sometimes little jets of colored steam shot out from the cracks underneath.

Grandpa Joe and Charlie were half running and half walking to keep up with Mr. Wonka, but they were able to read what it said on quite a few of the doors as they hurried by. EATABLE MARSHMALLOW PILLOWS, it said on one.

"Marshmallow pillows are terrific!" shouted Mr. Wonka as he dashed by. "They'll be all the rage when I get them into the shops! No time to go in, though! No time to go in!"

LICKABLE WALLPAPER FOR NURSERIES, it said on the next door.

"Lovely stuff, lickable wallpaper!" cried Mr. Wonka, rushing past. "It has pictures of fruits on it—bananas, apples, oranges, grapes, pineapples, strawberries, and snozzberries. . . ."

"*Snozzberries?*" said Mike Teavee.

"Don't interrupt!" said Mr. Wonka. "The wallpaper has pictures of all these fruits printed on it, and when you lick the picture of a banana, it tastes of banana. When you lick a strawberry, it tastes of strawberry. And when you lick a snozzberry, it tastes just exactly like a snozzberry. . . ."

"But what *does* a snozzberry taste like?"

"You're mumbling again," said Mr. Wonka. "Speak louder next time. On we go! Hurry up!"

HOT ICE CREAMS FOR COLD DAYS, it said on the next door.

"*Extremely* useful in the winter," said Mr. Wonka, rushing on. "Hot ice cream warms you up no end in freezing weather. I also make hot ice cubes for putting in hot drinks. Hot ice cubes make hot drinks hotter."

COWS THAT GIVE CHOCOLATE MILK, it said on the next door.

"Ah, my pretty little cows!" cried Mr. Wonka. "How I love those cows!"

"But why can't we *see* them?" asked Veruca Salt. "Why do we have to go rushing on past all these lovely rooms?"

"We shall stop in time!" called out Mr. Wonka. "Don't be so madly impatient!"

FIZZY LIFTING DRINKS, it said on the next door.

"Oh, those are fabulous!" cried Mr. Wonka. "They fill you with bubbles, and the bubbles are full of a special kind of gas, and this gas is so terrifically *lifting* that it lifts you right off the ground just like a balloon, and up you go until your head hits the ceiling—and there you stay."

"But how do you come down again?" asked little Charlie.

"You do a burp, of course," said Mr. Wonka. "You do a great big long rude burp, and *up* comes the gas and *down* comes you! But don't drink it outdoors! There's no knowing how high up you'll be carried if you do that. I gave some to an old Oompa-Loompa once out in the back yard and he went up and up and up and disappeared out of sight! It was very sad. I never saw him again."

"He should have burped," Charlie said.

"Of course he should have burped," said Mr. Wonka. "I stood there shouting, 'Burp, you silly ass, burp, or you'll never come down again! But he didn't or couldn't or wouldn't, I don't know which. Maybe he was too polite. He must be on the moon by now."

On the next door, it said, SQUARE CANDIES THAT LOOK ROUND.

"Wait!" cried Mr. Wonka, skidding suddenly to a halt. "I am very proud of my square candies that look round. Let's take a peek."

23
Square Candies That Look Round

EVERYBODY STOPPED and crowded to the door. The top half of the door was made of glass. Grandpa Joe lifted Charlie up so that he could get a better view, and looking in, Charlie saw a long table, and on the table there were rows and rows of small white square-shaped candies. The candies looked very much like square sugar lumps—except that each of them had a funny little pink face painted on one side. At the end of the table, a number of Oompa-Loompas were busily painting more faces on more candies.

"There you are!" cried Mr. Wonka. "Square candies that look round!"

"They don't look round to me," said Mike Teavee.

"They look square," said Veruca Salt. "They look completely square."

"But they *are* square," said Mr. Wonka. "I never said they weren't."

"You said they were *round*!" said Veruca Salt.

"I never said anything of the sort," said Mr. Wonka. "I said they *looked* round."

"But they *don't* look round!" said Veruca Salt. "They look square!"

"They look round," insisted Mr. Wonka.

"They most certainly do not look round!" cried Veruca Salt.

"Veruca, darling," said Mrs. Salt, "pay no attention to Mr. Wonka! He's lying to you!"

"My dear old fish," said Mr. Wonka, "go and boil your head!"

"How dare you speak to me like that!" shouted Mrs. Salt.

"Oh, do shut up," said Mr. Wonka. "Now watch this!" He took a key from his pocket, and unlocked the door, and flung it open . . . and suddenly . . . at the sound of the door opening, all the rows and rows of little square candies looked quickly round to see who was coming in. The tiny faces actually turned toward the door and stared at Mr. Wonka.

"There you are!" he cried triumphantly. "They're looking round! There's no argument about it! They are square candies that look round!"

"By golly, he's right!" said Grandpa Joe.

"Come on!" said Mr. Wonka, starting off down the corridor again. "On we go! We mustn't dawdle!"

BUTTERSCOTCH AND BUTTERGIN, it said on the next door they passed.

"Now *that* sounds a bit more interesting," said Mr. Salt, Veruca's father.

"Glorious stuff!" said Mr. Wonka. "The Oompa-Loompas all adore it. It makes them tiddly. Listen! You can hear them in there now, whooping it up."

Shrieks of laughter and snatches of singing could be heard coming through the closed door.

"They're drunk as lords," said Mr. Wonka. "They're drinking butterscotch and soda. They like that best of all.

Buttergin and tonic is also very popular. Follow me, please! We really mustn't keep stopping like this." He turned left. He turned right. They came to a long flight of stairs. Mr. Wonka slid down the bannisters. The three children did the same. Mrs. Salt and Mrs. Teavee, the only women now left in the party, were getting very out of breath. Mrs. Salt was a great fat creature with short legs, and she was blowing like a rhinoceros. "This way!" cried Mr. Wonka, turning left at the bottom of the stairs.

"Go *slower*!" panted Mrs. Salt.

"Impossible," said Mr. Wonka. "We should never get there in time if I did."

"Get where?" asked Veruca Salt.

"Never you mind," said Mr. Wonka. "You just wait and see."

24
Veruca in the Nut Room

MR. WONKA RUSHED ON down the corridor. THE NUT ROOM, it said on the next door they came to.

"All right," said Mr. Wonka, "stop here for a moment and catch your breath, and take a peek through the glass panel of this door. But don't go in! Whatever you do, don't go into THE NUT ROOM! If you go in, you'll disturb the squirrels!"

Everyone crowded around the door.

"Oh look, Grandpa, look!" cried Charlie.

"Squirrels!" shouted Veruca Salt.

"Jeepers!" said Mike Teavee.

It was an amazing sight. One hundred squirrels were seated upon high stools around a large table. On the table, there were mounds and mounds of walnuts, and the squirrels were all working away like mad, shelling the walnuts at a tremendous speed.

"These squirrels are specially trained for getting the nuts out of walnuts," Mr. Wonka explained.

"Why use squirrels?" Mike Teavee asked. "Why not use Oompa-Loompas?"

"Because," said Mr. Wonka, "Oompa-Loompas can't get walnuts out of walnut shells in one piece. They always break them in two. Nobody except squirrels can get walnuts *whole* out of walnut shells every time. It is extremely difficult. But in my factory, I insist upon using only whole walnuts. Therefore I have to have squirrels to do the job. Aren't they wonderful, the way they get those nuts out! And see how they first tap each walnut with their knuckles to be sure it's not a bad one! If it's bad, it makes a hollow sound, and they don't bother to open it. They just throw it down the garbage chute. There! Look! Watch that squirrel nearest to us! I think he's got a bad one now!"

They watched the little squirrel as he tapped the walnut shell with his knuckles. He cocked his head to one side, listening intently, then suddenly he threw the nut over his shoulder into a large hole in the floor.

"Hey, Mummy!" shouted Veruca Salt suddenly, "I've decided I want a squirrel! Get me one of those squirrels!"

"Don't be silly, sweetheart," said Mrs. Salt. "These all belong to Mr. Wonka."

"I don't care about that!" shouted Veruca. "I want one. All I've *got* at home is two dogs and four cats and six bunny rabbits and two parakeets and three canaries and a green parrot and a turtle and a bowl of goldfish and a cage of white mice and a silly old hamster! I want a *squirrel*!"

"All right, my pet," Mrs. Salt said soothingly. "Mummy'll get you a squirrel just as soon as she possibly can."

"But I don't want *any* old squirrel!" Veruca shouted. "I want a *trained* squirrel!"

At this point, Mr. Salt, Veruca's father, stepped forward. "Very well, Wonka," he said importantly, taking out a wallet full of money, "how much d'you want for one of these crazy squirrels? Name your price."

"They're not for sale," Mr. Wonka answered. "She can't have one."

"Who says I can't!" shouted Veruca. "I'm going in to grab me a squirrel this very minute!"

"Don't!" said Mr. Wonka quickly, but he was too late. The girl had already thrown open the door and rushed in.

The moment she entered the room, one hundred squirrels stopped what they were doing and turned their heads and stared at her with small black beady eyes.

Veruca Salt stopped also, and stared back at them.

Then her gaze fell upon a pretty little squirrel sitting nearest to her at the end of the table. The squirrel was holding a walnut in its paws.

"All right," Veruca said, "I'll have *you*!"

She reached out her hands to grab the squirrel . . . but as she did so . . . in that first split second when her hands started to go forward, there was a sudden flash of movement in the room, like a flash of brown lightning, and every single squirrel around the table took a flying leap towards her and landed on her body.

Twenty-five of them caught hold of her right arm, and pinned it down.

Twenty-five more caught hold of her left arm, and pinned that down.

Twenty-five caught hold of her right leg and anchored it to the ground.

Twenty-*four* caught hold of her left leg.

And the one remaining squirrel (obviously the leader of them all) climbed up on to her shoulder and started tap-tap-tapping the wretched girl's head with its knuckles.

"Save her!" screamed Mrs. Salt. "Veruca! Come back! What are they *doing* to her?"

"They're testing her to see if she's a bad nut," said Mr. Wonka. "You watch."

Veruca struggled furiously, but the squirrels held her tight and she couldn't move. The squirrel on her shoulder went tap-tap-tapping the side of her head with his knuckles.

Then all at once, the squirrels pulled Veruca to the ground and started carrying her across the floor.

"My goodness, she *is* a bad nut after all," said Mr. Wonka. "Her head must have sounded quite hollow."

Veruca kicked and screamed, but it was no use. The tiny strong paws held her tightly and she couldn't escape.

"Where are they taking her?" shrieked Mrs. Salt.

"She's going where all the other bad nuts go," said Mr. Willy Wonka. "Down the garbage chute."

"By golly, she *is* going down the chute!" said Mr. Salt, staring through the glass door at his daughter.

"Then save her!" cried Mrs. Salt.

"Too late," said Mr. Wonka. "She's gone!"

And indeed she had.

"But where?" shrieked Mrs. Salt, flapping her arms. "What happens to the bad nuts? Where does the chute go to?"

"That *particular* chute," Mr. Wonka told her, "runs directly into the great big main garbage pipe which carries away all the rubbish from every part of the factory—all the floor sweepings and potato peelings and rotten cabbages and fish heads and stuff like that."

"Who eats fish and cabbage and potatoes in *this* factory, I'd like to know?" said Mike Teavee.

"I do, of course," answered Mr. Wonka. "You don't think *I* live on cacao beans, do you?"

"But . . . but . . . but . . ." shrieked Mrs. Salt, "where does the great big pipe go to in the end?"

"Why, to the furnace, of course," Mr. Wonka said calmly. "To the incinerator."

Mrs. Salt opened her huge red mouth and started to scream.

"Don't worry," said Mr. Wonka, "there's always a chance that they've decided not to light it today."

"A *chance*!" yelled Mrs. Salt. "My darling Veruca! She'll . . . she'll . . . she'll be sizzled like a sausage!"

"Quite right, my dear," said Mr. Salt. "Now see here, Wonka," he added, "I think you've gone *just* a shade too far this time, I do indeed. My daughter may be a bit of a frump—I don't mind admitting it—but that doesn't mean you can roast her to a crisp. I'll have you know I'm extremely cross about this, I really am."

"Oh, don't be cross, my dear sir!" said Mr. Wonka. "I expect she'll turn up again sooner or later. She may not even have gone down at all. She may be stuck in the chute just below the entrance hole, and if *that's* the case, all you'll have to do is go in and pull her up again."

Hearing this, both Mr. and Mrs. Salt dashed into the Nut Room and ran over to the hole in the floor and peered in.

"Veruca!" shouted Mrs. Salt. "Are you down there!"

There was no answer.

Mrs. Salt bent further forward to get a closer look. She was now kneeling right on the edge of the hole with her head down and her enormous behind sticking up in the air like a giant mushroom. It was a dangerous position to be in. She needed only one tiny little push . . . one gentle nudge in the right place . . . and *that* is exactly what the squirrels gave her!

Over she toppled, into the hole head first, screeching like a parrot.

"Good gracious me!" said Mr. Salt, as he watched his fat wife go tumbling down the hole, "*what* a lot of garbage there's going to be today!" He saw her disappearing into the darkness. "What's it like down there, Angina?" he called out. He leaned further forward.

The squirrels rushed up behind him. . . .

"Help!" he shouted.

But he was already toppling forward, and down the chute he went, just as his wife had done before him—and his daughter.

"Oh *dear*!" cried Charlie, who was watching with the others through the door, "what on earth's going to happen to them now?"

"I expect someone will catch them at the bottom of the chute," said Mr. Wonka.

"But what about the great fiery incinerator?" asked Charlie.

"They only light it every other day," said Mr. Wonka. "Perhaps this is one of the days when they let it go out. You never know . . . they might be lucky. . . ."

"Ssshh!" said Grandpa Joe. "Listen! Here comes another song!"

From far away down the corridor came the beating of drums. Then the singing began.

> *"Veruca Salt!" sang the Oompa-Loompas.*
> *"Veruca Salt, the little brute,*
> *Has just gone down the garbage chute,*
> *(And as we very rightly thought*
> *That in a case like this we ought*
> *To see the thing completely through,*
> *We've polished off her parents, too.)*
> *Down goes Veruca! Down the drain!*
> *And here, perhaps, we should explain*
> *That she will meet, as she descends,*
> *A rather different set of friends*

To those that she has left behind—
These *won't be nearly so refined.*
A fish head, for example, cut
This morning from a halibut.
'Hello! Good morning! How d'you do?
How nice to meet you! How are you?'
And then a little further down
A mass of others gather round:
A bacon rind, some rancid lard,
A loaf of bread gone stale and hard,
A steak that nobody could chew,
An oyster from an oyster stew,
Some liverwurst so old and gray
One smelled it from a mile away,
A rotten nut, a reeky pear,
A thing the cat left on the stair,
And lots of other things as well,
Each with a rather horrid smell.
These *are Veruca's new found friends*
That she will meet as she descends,
And this *is the price she has to pay*
For going so very far astray.
But now, my dears, we think you might
Be wondering—is it really right
That every single bit of blame
And all the scolding and the shame
Should fall upon Veruca Salt?
Is she *the only one at fault?*
For though she's spoiled, and dreadfully so,
A girl can't spoil herself, you know.
Who *spoiled her, then? Ah, who indeed?*

Who pandered to her every need?
Who turned her into such a brat?
Who are the culprits? Who did that?
Alas! You needn't look so far
To find out who these sinners are.
They are (and this is very sad)
Her loving parents, MUM and DAD.
And that is why we're glad they fell
Into the garbage chute as well.

25
The Great Glass Elevator

"I'VE NEVER SEEN anything like it!" cried Mr. Wonka. "The children are disappearing like rabbits! But you mustn't worry about it! They'll *all* come out in the wash!"

Mr. Wonka looked at the little group that stood beside him in the corridor. There were only two children left now—Mike Teavee and Charlie Bucket. And there were three grownups, Mr. and Mrs. Teavee and Grandpa Joe. "Shall we move on?" Mr. Wonka asked.

"Oh, yes!" cried Charlie and Grandpa Joe, both together.

"My feet are getting tired," said Mike Teavee. "I want to watch television."

"If you're tired then we'd better take the elevator," said Mr. Wonka. "It's over here. Come on! In we go!" He skipped across the passage to a pair of double doors. The doors slid open. The two children and the grownups went in.

"Now then," cried Mr. Wonka, "which button shall we press first? Take your pick!"

Charlie Bucket stared around him in astonishment. This was the craziest elevator he had ever seen. There were buttons everywhere! The walls, and even the *ceiling,* were covered all over with rows and rows and rows of small, black push buttons! There must have been a thousand of them on each wall, and another thousand on the ceiling! And now Charlie noticed that every single button had a tiny printed label beside it telling you which room you would be taken to if you pressed it.

"This isn't just an ordinary up-and-down elevator!" announced Mr. Wonka proudly. "This elevator can go sideways and longways and slantways and any other way you can think of! It can visit any single room in the whole factory, no matter where it is! You simply press the button . . . and *zing*! . . . you're off!"

"*Fantastic*!" murmured Grandpa Joe. His eyes were shining with excitement as he stared at the rows and rows of buttons.

"The whole elevator is made of thick, clear glass!" Mr. Wonka declared. "Walls, doors, ceiling, floor, everything is made of glass so that you can see out!"

"But there's nothing to see," said Mike Teavee.

"Choose a button!" said Mr. Wonka. "The two children may press one button each. So take your pick! Hurry up! In every room, something delicious and wonderful is being made."

Quickly, Charlie started reading some of the labels alongside the buttons.

THE ROCK-CANDY MINE—10,000 FEET DEEP, it said on one.

COKERNUT-ICE SKATING RINKS, it said on another.

Then . . . STRAWBERRY-JUICE WATER PISTOLS.

TOFFEE-APPLE TREES FOR PLANTING OUT IN YOUR GARDEN—ALL SIZES.

EXPLODING CANDY FOR YOUR ENEMIES.

LUMINOUS LOLLIES FOR EATING IN BED AT NIGHT.

MINT JUJUBES FOR THE BOY NEXT DOOR—THEY'LL GIVE HIM GREEN TEETH FOR A MONTH.

CAVITY-FILLING CARAMELS—NO MORE DENTISTS.

STICKJAW FOR TALKATIVE PARENTS.

WRIGGLE-SWEETS THAT WRIGGLE DELIGHTFULLY IN YOUR TUMMY AFTER SWALLOWING.

INVISIBLE CHOCOLATE BARS FOR EATING IN CLASS.

CANDY-COATED PENCILS FOR SUCKING.

FIZZY LEMONADE SWIMMING POOLS.

MAGIC HAND-FUDGE—WHEN YOU HOLD IT IN YOUR HAND, YOU TASTE IT IN YOUR MOUTH.

RAINBOW DROPS—SUCK THEM AND YOU CAN SPIT IN SIX DIFFERENT COLORS.

"Come on, come on!" cried Mr. Wonka. "We can't wait all day!"

"Isn't there a *Television Room* in all this lot?" asked Mike Teavee.

"Certainly there's a television room," Mr. Wonka said. "That button over there." He pointed with his finger. Everybody looked. TELEVISION CHOCOLATE, it said on the tiny label beside the button.

"*Whoopee!*" shouted Mike Teavee. "That's for me!" He stuck out his thumb and pressed the button. Instantly, there was a tremendous whizzing noise. The doors clanged shut and the elevator leaped away as though it had been stung by a wasp. But it leapt *sideways*! And all the passengers (except Mr. Wonka, who was holding onto a strap from the ceiling) were flung off their feet onto the floor.

"Get up, get up!" cried Mr. Wonka, roaring with laughter. But just as they were staggering to their feet, the elevator changed directions and swerved violently round a corner. And over they went once more.

"Help!" shouted Mrs. Teavee.

"Take my hand, madam," said Mr. Wonka gallantly.

"There you are! Now grab this strap! Everybody grab a strap. The journey's not over yet!"

Old Grandpa Joe staggered to his feet and caught hold of a strap. Little Charlie, who couldn't possibly reach as high as that, put his arms around Grandpa Joe's legs and hung on tight.

The elevator rushed on at the speed of a rocket. Now it was beginning to climb. It was shooting up and up and up on a steep slanty course as if it were climbing a very steep hill. Then suddenly, as though it had come to the top of the hill and gone over a precipice, it dropped like a stone and Charlie felt his tummy coming right up into his throat, and Grandpa Joe shouted, "Yippee! Here we go!" And Mrs. Teavee cried out, "The rope has broken! We're going to crash!" And Mr. Wonka said, "Calm yourself, my dear lady," and patted her comfortingly on the arm. And then Grandpa Joe looked down at Charlie who was clinging to his legs, and he said, "Are you all right, Charlie?" Charlie shouted, "I love it! It's like being on a roller coaster!" And through the glass walls of the elevator, as it rushed along, they caught sudden glimpses of strange and wonderful things going on in some of the other rooms:

An enormous spout with brown sticky stuff oozing out of it onto the floor. . . .

A great, craggy mountain made entirely of fudge, with Oompa-Loompas (all roped together for safety) hacking huge hunks of fudge out of its sides. . . .

A machine with white powder spraying out of it like a snowstorm. . . .

A lake of hot caramel with steam coming off it. . . .

A village of Oompa-Loompas, with tiny houses and streets and hundreds of Oompa-Loompa children no more than four inches high playing in the streets. . . .

And now the elevator began flattening out again, but it seemed to be going faster than ever, and Charlie could hear the scream of the wind outside as it hurtled forward . . . and it twisted . . . and it turned . . . and it went up . . . and it went down . . . and . . .

"I'm going to be sick!" yelled Mrs. Teavee, turning green in the face.

"Please don't be sick," said Mr. Wonka.

"Try and stop me!" said Mrs. Teavee.

"Then you'd better take this," said Mr. Wonka, and he swept his magnificent black top hat off his head, and held it out, upside down, in front of Mrs. Teavee's mouth.

"Make this awful thing stop!" ordered Mr. Teavee.

"Can't do that," said Mr. Wonka. "It won't stop till we get there. I only hope no one's using the *other* elevator at this moment."

"What other elevator?" screamed Mrs. Teavee.

"The one that goes the opposite way on the same track as this one," said Mr. Wonka.

"Holy mackerel!" cried Mr. Teavee. "You mean we might have a collision?"

"I've always been lucky so far," said Mr. Wonka.

"Now I *am* going to be sick!" yelled Mrs. Teavee.

"No, no!" said Mr. Wonka. "Not now! We're nearly there! Don't spoil my hat!"

The next moment, there was a screaming of brakes, and the elevator began to slow down. Then it stopped altogether.

"Some ride!" said Mr. Teavee, wiping his great sweaty face with a handkerchief.

"Never again!" gasped Mrs. Teavee. And then the doors of the elevator slid open and Mr. Wonka said, "Just a minute now! Listen to me! I want everybody to be very careful in this room. There is dangerous stuff around in here and you *must not* tamper with it."

26
The Television-Chocolate Room

THE TEAVEE FAMILY, together with Charlie and Grandpa Joe, stepped out of the elevator into a room so dazzlingly bright and dazzlingly white that they screwed up their eyes in pain and stopped walking. Mr. Wonka handed each of them a pair of dark glasses and said, "Put these on quick! And don't take them off in here whatever you do! This light could blind you!"

As soon as Charlie had his dark glasses on, he was able to look around him in comfort. He saw a long narrow room. The room was painted white all over. Even the floor was white, and there wasn't a speck of dust anywhere. From the ceiling, huge lamps hung down and bathed the room in a brilliant blue-white light. The room was completely bare except at the far ends. At one of these ends there was an enormous camera on wheels, and a whole army of Oompa-Loompas was clustering around it, oiling its joints and adjusting its knobs and polishing its great glass lens. The Oompa-Loompas were all dressed in the most extraordinary way. They were wearing bright-red space suits, complete with helmets and goggles—at least they looked like space suits—and they were working in complete silence. Watching them, Charlie experienced a queer sense of danger. There was something dangerous about this whole business, and the Oompa-Loompas knew it. There was no chattering or singing among them here, and they moved about over the huge black camera slowly and carefully in their scarlet space suits.

At the other end of the room, about fifty paces away from the camera, a single Oompa-Loompa (also wearing a space suit) was sitting at a black table gazing at the screen of a very large television set.

"Here we go!" cried Mr. Wonka, hopping up and down with excitement. "This is the Testing Room for my very latest and greatest invention—Television Chocolate!"

"But what *is* Television Chocolate?" asked Mike Teavee.

"Good heavens, child, stop interrupting me!" said Mr. Wonka. "It works by television. I don't like television myself. I suppose it's all right in small doses, but children never seem to be able to take it in small doses. They want to sit there all day long staring and staring at the screen. . . ."

"That's me!" said Mike Teavee.

"Shut up!" said Mr. Teavee.

"Thank you," said Mr. Wonka. "I shall now tell you how this amazing television set of mine works. But first of all, do you know how ordinary television works? It is very simple. At one end, where the picture is being taken, you have a large movie camera and you start photographing something. The photographs are then split up into millions of tiny little pieces which are so small that you can't see them, and these little pieces are shot out into the sky by electricity. In the sky, they go whizzing around all over the place until suddenly they hit the antenna on the roof of somebody's house. They then go flashing down the wire that leads right into the back of the television set, and in there they get jiggled and joggled around until at last every single one of those millions of tiny pieces is fitted back into its right place (just like a jigsaw puzzle), and presto!—the photograph appears on the screen. . . ."

"That isn't *exactly* how it works," Mike Teavee said.

"I am a little deaf in my left ear," Mr. Wonka said. "You must forgive me if I don't hear everything you say."

"I said, that isn't *exactly* how it works!" shouted Mike Teavee.

"You're a nice boy," Mr. Wonka said, "but you talk too much. Now then! The very first time I saw ordinary television working, I was struck by a tremendous idea. 'Look here!' I shouted, 'if these people can break up a *photograph* into millions of pieces and send the pieces whizzing through the air and then put them together again at the other end, why can't *I* do the same thing with a bar of chocolate? Why can't *I* send a real bar of chocolate whizzing through the air in tiny pieces and then put the pieces together at the other end, all ready to be eaten?"

"Impossible!" said Mike Teavee.

"You think so?" cried Mr. Wonka. "Well, watch this! I shall now send a bar of my very best chocolate from one end of this room to the other—by television! Get ready, there! Bring in the chocolate!"

Immediately, six Oompa-Loompas marched forward carrying on their shoulders the most enormous bar of chocolate Charlie had ever seen. It was about the size of the mattress he slept on at home.

"It has to be big," Mr. Wonka explained, "because whenever you send something by television, it always comes out much smaller than it was when it went in. Even with *ordinary* television, when you photograph a big man, he never comes out on your screen any taller than a pencil, does he? Here we go, then! Get ready! *No, no! Stop! Hold everything!* You there! Mike Teavee! Stand back! You're too close to the camera! There are dangerous rays coming out of that thing! They could break you up into million tiny pieces in one second! That's why the Oompa-Loompas are wearing space suits! The suits protect them! All right! That's better! Now, then! *Switch on!*"

One of the Oompa-Loompas caught hold of a large switch and pulled it down.

There was a blinding flash.

"The chocolate's gone!" shouted Grandpa Joe, waving his arms.

He was quite right! The whole enormous bar of chocolate had disappeared completely into thin air!

"It's on its way!" cried Mr. Wonka. "It is now rushing through the air above our heads in a million tiny pieces. Quick! Come over here!" He dashed over to the other end of the room where the large television set was standing, and the others followed him. "Watch the screen!" he cried. "Here it comes! Look!"

The screen flickered and lit up. Then suddenly, a small bar of chocolate appeared in the middle of the screen.

"Take it!" shouted Mr. Wonka, growing more and more excited.

"How can you take it?" asked Mike Teavee, laughing.

"It's just a picture on a television screen!"

"Charlie Bucket!" cried Mr. Wonka. "*You* take it! Reach out and grab it!"

Charlie put out his hand and touched the screen, and suddenly, miraculously, the bar of chocolate came away in his fingers. He was so surprised he nearly dropped it.

"Eat it!" shouted Mr. Wonka. "Go on and eat it! It'll be delicious! It's the same bar! It's gotten smaller on the journey, that's all!"

"It's absolutely fantastic!" gasped Grandpa Joe. "It's . . . it's . . . it's a miracle!"

"Just imagine," cried Mr. Wonka, "when I start using this across the country . . . you'll be sitting at home watching television and suddenly a commercial will flash onto the screen and a voice will say, 'EAT WONKA'S CHOCOLATES! THEY'RE THE BEST IN THE WORLD! IF YOU DON'T BELIEVE US, TRY ONE FOR YOURSELF—*NOW*!' And you simply reach out and take one! How about that, eh?"

"Terrific!" cried Grandpa Joe. "It will change the world!"

27
Mike Teavee is Sent by Television

MIKE TEAVEE was even more excited than Grandpa Joe at seeing a bar of chocolate being sent by television.

"But Mr. Wonka," he shouted, "can you send *other things* through the air in the same way? Breakfast cereal, for instance?"

"Oh, my sainted aunt!" cried Mr. Wonka. "Don't mention that disgusting stuff in front of me! Do you *know* what breakfast cereal is made of? It's made of all those little curly wooden shavings you find in pencil sharpeners!"

"But could you send it by television if you wanted to, as you do chocolate?" asked Mike Teavee.

"Of course I could!"

"And what about people?" asked Mike Teavee. "Could you send a real live person from one place to another in the same way?"

"A *person*!" cried Mr. Wonka. "Are you off your rocker?"

"But *could* it be done?"

"Good heavens, child, I really don't know . . . I suppose it *could* . . . yes, I'm pretty sure it could . . . of course it could . . . I wouldn't like to risk it, though . . . it might have some very nasty results. . . ."

But Mike Teavee was already off and running. The moment he heard Mr. Wonka saying, "I'm pretty sure it could . . . of course it could," he turned away and started running as fast as he could towards the other end of the room where the great camera was standing. "Look at me!" he shouted as he ran. "I'm going to be the first person in the world to be sent by television!"

"No, no, no, no!" cried Mr. Wonka.

"Mike!" screamed Mrs. Teavee. "Stop! Come back! You'll be turned into a million tiny pieces!"

But there was no stopping Mike Teavee now. The crazy

boy rushed on, and when he reached the enormous camera, he jumped straight for the switch, scattering Oompa-Loompas right and left as he went.

"See you later, alligator!" he shouted, and he pulled down the switch, and as he did so, he leaped out into the full glare of the mighty lens.

There was a blinding flash.

Then there was silence.

Then Mrs. Teavee ran forward . . . but she stopped dead in the middle of the room . . . and she stood there . . . she stood staring at the place where her son had been . . . and her great red mouth opened wide and she screamed, "He's gone! He's gone!"

"Great heavens, he *has* gone!" shouted Mr. Teavee.

Mr. Wonka hurried forward and placed a hand gently on Mrs. Teavee's shoulder. "We shall have to hope for the best," he said. "We must pray that your little boy will come out unharmed at the other end."

"Mike!" screamed Mrs. Teavee, clasping her head in her hands. "Where are you?"

"I'll tell you where he is," said Mr. Teavee, "he's whizzing around above our heads in a million tiny pieces!"

"Don't talk about it!" wailed Mrs. Teavee.

"We must watch the television set," said Mr. Wonka. "He may come through any moment."

Mr. and Mrs. Teavee and Grandpa Joe and little Charlie and Mr. Wonka all gathered round the television and stared tensely at the screen. The screen was quite blank.

"He's taking a heck of a long time to come across," said Mr. Teavee, wiping his brow.

"Oh dear, oh dear," said Mr. Wonka, "I do hope that no part of him gets left behind."

"What on earth do you mean?" asked Mr. Teavee sharply.

"I don't wish to alarm you," said Mr. Wonka, "but it does sometimes happen that only about half the little pieces find their way into the television set. It happened last week. I don't know why, but the result was that only half a bar of chocolate came through."

Mrs. Teavee let out a scream of horror. "You mean only a half of Mike is coming back to us?" she cried.

"Let's hope it's the top half," said Mr. Teavee.

"Hold everything!" said Mr. Wonka. "Watch the screen! Something's happening!"

The screen had suddenly begun to flicker.

Then some wavy lines appeared.

Mr. Wonka adjusted one of the knobs and the wavy lines went away.

And now, very slowly, the screen began to get brighter and brighter.

"Here he comes!" yelled Mr. Wonka. "Yes, that's him all right!"

"Is he all in one piece?" cried Mrs. Teavee.

"I'm not sure," said Mr. Wonka. "It's too early to tell."

Faintly at first, but becoming clearer and clearer every second, the picture of Mike Teavee appeared on the screen. He was standing up and waving at the audience and grinning from ear to ear.

"But he's a midget!" shouted Mr. Teavee.

"Mike," cried Mrs. Teavee, "are you all right? Are there any bits of you missing?"

"Isn't he going to get any bigger?" shouted Mr. Teavee.

"Talk to me, Mike!" cried Mrs. Teavee. "Say something! Tell me you're all right!"

A tiny little voice, no louder than the squeaking of a mouse, came out of the television set. "Hi, Mum!" it said. "Hi, Pop! Look at *me*! I'm the first person ever to be sent by television!"

"Grab him!" ordered Mr. Wonka. "Quick!"

Mrs. Teavee shot out a hand and picked the tiny figure of Mike Teavee out of the screen.

"Hooray!" cried Mr. Wonka. "He's all in one piece! He's completely unharmed!"

"You call *that* unharmed?" snapped Mrs. Teavee, peering at the little speck of a boy who was now running to and fro across the palm of her hand, waving his pistols in the air.

He was certainly not more than an inch tall.

"He's *shrunk*!" said Mr. Teavee.

"Of course he's shrunk," said Mr. Wonka. "What did you expect?"

"This is terrible!" wailed Mrs. Teavee. "What *are* we going to do?"

And Mr. Teavee said, "We can't send him back to school like this! He'll get trod upon! He'll get squashed!"

"He won't be able to do *anything*!" cried Mrs. Teavee.

"Oh, yes I will!" squeaked the tiny voice of Mike Teavee. "I'll still be able to watch television!"

"Never again!" shouted Mr. Teavee. "I'm throwing the television set right out the window the moment we get home. I've had enough of television!"

When he heard this, Mike Teavee flew into a terrible tantrum. He started jumping up and down on the palm of his mother's hand, screaming and yelling and trying to bite her fingers. "I want to watch television!" he squeaked. "I want to watch television! I want to watch television! I want to watch television!"

"Here! Give him to me!" said Mr. Teavee, and he took the tiny boy and shoved him into the breast pocket of his jacket and stuffed a handkerchief on top. Squeals and yells came from inside the pocket, and the pocket shook as the furious little prisoner fought to get out.

"Oh, Mr. Wonka," wailed Mrs. Teavee, "how can we make him grow?"

"Well," said Mr. Wonka, stroking his beard and gazing thoughtfully at the ceiling, "I must say that's a wee bit tricky. But small boys are extremely springy and elastic. They stretch like mad. So what we'll do, we'll put him in a special machine I have for testing the stretchiness of chewing gum! Maybe that will bring him back to what he was."

"Oh, thank you!" said Mrs. Teavee.

"Don't mention it, dear lady."

"How far d'you think he'll stretch?" asked Mr. Teavee.

"Maybe miles," said Mr. Wonka. "Who knows? But he's

going to be awfully thin. Everything gets thinner when you stretch it."

"You mean like chewing gum?" asked Mr. Teavee.

"Exactly."

"How thin will he be?" asked Mrs. Teavee anxiously.

"I haven't the foggiest idea," said Mr. Wonka. "And it doesn't really matter, anyway, because we'll soon fatten him up again. All we'll have to do is give him a triple over-dose of my wonderful Supervitamin Candy. Supervitamin Candy contains huge amounts of vitamin A and vitamin B. It also contains vitamin C, vitamin D, vitamin E, vitamin F, vitamin G, vitamin I, vitamin J, vitamin K, vitamin L, vita-min M, vitamin N, vitamin O, vitamin P, vitamin Q, vitamin R, vitamin T, vitamin U, vitamin V, vitamin W, vitamin X, vit-amin Y, *and,* believe it or not, vitamin Z! The only two vit-amins it doesn't have in it are vitamin S, because it makes you sick, and vitamin H, because it makes you grow horns out of the top of your head, like a bull. But it *does* have in it a very small amount of the rarest and most magical vit-amin of them all—vitamin Wonka."

"And what will *that* do to him?" asked Mr. Teavee anx-iously.

"It'll make his toes grow out until they're as long as his fingers. . . ."

"Oh, no!" cried Mrs. Teavee.

"Don't be silly," said Mr. Wonka. "It's most useful. He'll be able to play the piano with his feet."

"But Mr. Wonka. . . ."

"No arguments, *please*!" said Mr. Wonka. He turned away and clicked his fingers three times in the air. An

Oompa-Loompa appeared immediately and stood beside him. "Follow these orders," said Mr. Wonka, handing the Oompa-Loompa a piece of paper on which he had written full instructions. "And you'll find the boy in his father's pocket. Off you go! Good-by, Mr. Teavee! Good-by, Mrs. Teavee! And please don't look so worried! They all come out in the wash, you know; every one of them. . . ."

At the end of the room, the Oompa-Loompas around the giant camera were already beating their tiny drums and beginning to jog up and down to the rhythm.

"There they go again!" said Mr. Wonka. "I'm afraid you can't stop them singing."

Little Charlie caught Grandpa Joe's hand, and the two of them stood beside Mr. Wonka in the middle of the long bright room, listening to the Oompa-Loompas. And this is what they sang:

"The most important thing we've learned,
So far as children are concerned,
Is never, NEVER, NEVER let
Them near your television set—
Or better still, just don't install
The idiotic thing at all.
In almost every house we've been,
We've watched them gaping at the screen.
They loll and slop and lounge about,
And stare until their eyes pop out.
(Last week in someone's place we saw
A dozen eyeballs on the floor.)

They sit and stare and stare and sit
Until they're hypnotised by it,
Until they're absolutely drunk
With all that shocking ghastly junk.
Oh yes, we know it keeps them still,
They don't climb out the window sill,
They never fight or kick or punch,
They leave you free to cook the lunch
And wash the dishes in the sink—
But did you ever *stop to think,*
To wonder just exactly what
This does to your beloved tot?
IT ROTS THE SENSES IN THE HEAD!
IT KILLS IMAGINATION DEAD!
IT CLOGS AND CLUTTERS UP THE MIND!
IT MAKES A CHILD SO DULL AND BLIND
HE CAN NO LONGER UNDERSTAND
A FANTASY, A FAIRYLAND!
HIS BRAIN BECOMES AS SOFT AS CHEESE!
HIS POWERS OF THINKING RUST AND FREEZE!
HE CANNOT THINK—HE ONLY SEES!
'All right!' you'll cry. 'All right!' you'll say,
'But if *we take the set away,*
What shall we do to entertain
Our darling children? Please explain!'
We'll answer this by asking you,
'What used *the darling ones to do?*
'How used *they keep themselves contented*
Before this monster was invented?'
Have you forgotten? Don't you know?

We'll say it very loud and slow:
THEY ... USED ... TO ... READ! They'd READ and
    READ,
AND READ and READ, and then proceed
To READ some more. Great Scott! Gadzooks!
One half their lives was reading books!
The nursery shelves held books galore!
Books cluttered up the nursery floor!
And in the bedroom, by the bed,
More books were waiting to be read!
Such wondrous, fine, fantastic tales
Of dragons, gypsies, queens, and whales
And treasure isles, and distant shores
Where smugglers rowed with muffled oars,
And pirates wearing purple pants,
And sailing ships and elephants,
And cannibals crouching 'round the pot,
Stirring away at something hot.
(It smells so good, what can it be!
Good gracious, it's Penelope.)
The younger ones had Beatrix Potter
With Mr. Tod, the dirty rotter,
And Squirrel Nutkin, Pigling Bland,
And Mrs. Tiggy-Winkle and—
Just How The Camel Got His Hump,
And How The Monkey Lost His Rump,
And Mr. Toad, and bless my soul,
There's Mr. Rat and Mr. Mole—
Oh, books, what books they used to know,
Those children living long ago!

So please, oh please, we beg, we pray,
Go throw your TV set away,
And in its place you can install
A lovely bookshelf on the wall.
Then fill the shelves with lots of books,
Ignoring all the dirty looks,
The screams and yells, the bites and kicks,
And children hitting you with sticks—
Fear not, because we promise you
That, in about a week or two
Of having nothing else to do,
They'll now begin to feel the need
Of having something good to read.
And once they start—oh boy, oh boy!
You watch the slowly growing joy
That fills their hearts. They'll grow so keen
They'll wonder what they'd ever seen
In that ridiculous machine,
That nauseating, foul, unclean,
Repulsive television screen!
And later, each and every kid
Will love you more for what you did.
P.S. Regarding Mike Teavee,
We very much regret that we
Shall simply have to wait and see
If we can get him back his height.
But if we can't—it serves him right.

28
Only Charlie Left

"WHICH ROOM SHALL IT BE NEXT?" said Mr. Wonka as he turned away and darted into the elevator. "Come on! Hurry up! We *must* get going! And how many children are there left now?"

Little Charlie looked at Grandpa Joe, and Grandpa Joe looked back at little Charlie.

"But Mr. Wonka," Grandpa Joe called after him, "there's . . . there's only Charlie left now."

Mr. Wonka swung round and stared at Charlie.

There was a silence. Charlie stood there holding tightly onto Grandpa Joe's hand.

"You mean you're the *only* one left?" Mr. Wonka said, pretending to be surprised.

"Why yes," whispered Charlie. "Yes."

Mr. Wonka suddenly exploded with excitement. "But my *dear boy,*" he cried out, "*that means you've won*!" He rushed out of the elevator and started shaking Charlie's hand so furiously it nearly came off. "Oh, I do congratulate you!" he cried. "I really do! I'm absolutely delighted! It couldn't be better! How wonderful this is! I had a hunch, you know, right from the beginning, that it was going to be you! Well *done,* Charlie, well *done*! This is terrific! Now the fun is really going to start! But we mustn't dilly! We mustn't dally! There's even less time to lose now than there was before! We have an *enormous* number of things to do before the day is out! Just think of the *arrangements* that have to be made! And the people we have to fetch! But luckily for us, we have the great glass elevator to speed things up! Jump in, my dear Charlie, jump in! You too, Grandpa Joe, sir! No, no, *after* you! That's the way! Now then! This time *I* shall choose the button we are going to press!" Mr. Wonka's bright twinkling blue eyes rested for a moment on Charlie's face.

Something crazy is going to happen now, Charlie thought. But he wasn't frightened. He wasn't even nervous. He was just terrifically excited. And so was Grandpa Joe. The old man's face was shining with excitement as he watched every move that Mr. Wonka made. Mr. Wonka was reaching for a button high up on the glass ceiling of the elevator. Charlie and Grandpa Joe both craned their necks to read what it said on the little label beside the button.

It said . . . UP AND OUT.

"*Up* and *out*," thought Charlie, "What sort of a room is that?"

Mr. Wonka pressed the button.

The glass doors closed.

"Hold on!" cried Mr. Wonka.

Then *WHAM*! The elevator shot straight up like a rocket! "Yippee!" shouted Grandpa Joe. Charlie was clinging to Grandpa Joe's legs and Mr. Wonka was holding onto a strap from the ceiling, and up they went, up, up, up, straight up this time, with no twistings or turnings, and Charlie could hear the whistling of the air outside as the elevator went faster and faster. "Yippee!" shouted Grandpa Joe again. "Yippee! Here we go!"

"Faster!" cried Mr. Wonka, banging the wall of the elevator with his hand. "Faster! Faster! If we don't go any faster than this, we shall never get through!"

"Through what?" shouted Grandpa Joe. "What have we got to get through?"

"Ah-ha!" cried Mr. Wonka, "you wait and see! I've been *longing* to press this button for years! But I've never done it until now! I was tempted many times! Oh yes, I was tempted! But I couldn't bear the thought of making a great big hole in the roof of the factory! Here we go, boys! Up and out!"

"But you don't mean . . ." shouted Grandpa Joe, ". . . you don't *really* mean that this elevator . . ."

"Oh yes, I do!" answered Mr. Wonka. "You wait and see! Up and out!"

"But . . . but . . . but . . . it's made of glass!" shouted Grandpa Joe. "It'll break into a million pieces!"

"I suppose it might," said Mr. Wonka, cheerful as ever, "but it's pretty thick glass, all the same."

The elevator rushed on, going up and up and up, faster and faster and faster. . . .

Then suddenly, CRASH!—and the most tremendous noise of splintering wood and broken tiles came from directly above their heads, and Grandpa Joe shouted, "Help! It's the end! We're done for!" and Mr. Wonka said, "No, we're not! We're through! We're out!" Sure enough, the elevator had shot right up through the roof of the factory and was now rising into the sky like a rocket, and the sunshine was pouring in through the glass roof. In five seconds they were a thousand feet up in the sky.

"The elevator's gone mad!" shouted Grandpa Joe.

"Have no fear, my dear sir," said Mr. Wonka calmly, and he pressed another button. The elevator stopped. It stopped and hung in mid-air, hovering like a helicopter, hovering over the factory and over the very town itself which lay spread out below them like a picture postcard! Looking down through the glass floor on which he was standing, Charlie could see the small far-away houses and the streets and the snow that lay thickly over everything.

It was an eerie and frightening feeling to be standing on clear glass high up in the sky. It made you feel that you weren't standing on anything at all.

"Are we all right?" cried Grandpa Joe. "How does this thing stay up?"

"Candy power!" said Mr. Wonka. "One million candy power! Oh, look," he cried, pointing down, "there go the other children! They're returning home!"

29
The Other Children Go Home

"WE *MUST* GO DOWN and take a look at our little friends before we do anything else," said Mr. Wonka. He pressed a different button, and the elevator dropped lower, and soon it was hovering just above the entrance gates to the factory.

Looking down now, Charlie could see the children and their parents standing in a little group just inside the gates. "I can only see three," he said. "Who's missing?"

"I expect it's Mike Teavee," Mr. Wonka said. "But he'll be coming along soon. Do you see the trucks?" Mr. Wonka pointed to a line of gigantic covered vans parked in a line nearby.

"Yes," Charlie said. "What are *they* for?"

"Don't you remember what it said on the Golden Tickets? Every child goes home with a lifetime's supply of candy. There's one truckload for each of them, loaded to the brim. Ah-ha," Mr. Wonka went on, "there goes our friend Augustus Gloop! D'you see him? He's getting into the first truck with his mother and father!"

"You mean he's *really* all right?" asked Charlie, astonished. "Even after going up that awful pipe?"

"He's very much all right," said Mr. Wonka.

"He's changed!" said Grandpa Joe, peering down through the glass wall of the elevator. "He used to be fat! Now he's thin as a straw!"

"Of course he's changed," said Mr. Wonka, laughing. "He got squeezed in the pipe. Don't you remember? And look! There goes Miss Violet Beauregarde, the great gum-chewer! It seems as though they managed to de-juice her after all. I'm so glad. And how healthy she looks! Much better than before!"

"But she's purple in the face!" cried Grandpa Joe.

"So she is," said Mr. Wonka. "Ah, well, there's nothing we can do about that."

"Good gracious!" cried Charlie. "Look at poor Veruca Salt and Mr. Salt and Mrs. Salt! They're simply *covered* with garbage!"

"And here comes Mike Teavee!" said Grandpa Joe. "Good heavens! What *have* they done to him? He's about ten feet tall and thin as a wire!"

"They've overstretched him on the gum-stretching machine," said Mr. Wonka. "How very careless."

"But how dreadful for him!" cried Charlie.

"Nonsense," said Mr. Wonka, "he's very lucky. Every basketball team in the country will be trying to get him. But now," he added, "it is time we left these four silly children. I have something very important to talk to you about, my dear Charlie." Mr. Wonka pressed another button, and the elevator swung upwards into the sky.

30

Charlie's Chocolate Factory

THE GREAT GLASS ELEVATOR was now hovering high over the town. Inside the elevator stood Mr. Wonka, Grandpa Joe, and little Charlie.

"How I love my chocolate factory," said Mr. Wonka, gazing down. Then he paused, and he turned around and looked at Charlie with a most serious expression on his face. "Do *you* love it, too, Charlie?" he asked.

"Oh, yes," cried Charlie, "I think it's the most wonderful place in the whole world!"

"I am very pleased to hear you say that," said Mr. Wonka, looking more serious than ever. He went on staring at Charlie. "Yes," he said, "I am very pleased indeed to hear you say that. And now I shall tell you why." Mr. Wonka cocked his head to one side and all at once the tiny twinkling wrinkles of a smile appeared around the corners of his eyes, and he said, "You see, my dear boy, I have decided to make you a present of the whole place.

As soon as you are old enough to run it, the entire factory will become yours."

Charlie stared at Mr. Wonka. Grandpa Joe opened his mouth to speak, but no words came out.

"It's quite true," Mr. Wonka said, smiling broadly now. "I really am giving it to you. That's all right, isn't it?"

"*Giving* it to him?" gasped Grandpa Joe. "You must be joking."

"I'm not joking, sir. I'm deadly serious."

"But . . . but . . . why should you want to give your factory to little Charlie?"

"Listen," Mr. Wonka said, "I'm an old man. I'm much older than you think. I can't go on forever. I've got no children of my own, no family at all. So who is going to run the factory when I get too old to do it myself? *Someone's* got to keep it going—if only for the sake of the Oompa-Loompas. Mind you, there are thousands of clever men who would give anything for the chance to come in and take over from me, but I don't *want* that sort of person. I don't want a grown-up person at all. A grownup won't listen to me; he won't learn. He will try to do things his own way and not mine. So I have to have a child. I want a good sensible loving child, one to whom I can tell all my most precious candy-making secrets—while I am still alive."

"So *that* is why you sent out the Golden Tickets!" cried Charlie.

"Exactly!" said Mr. Wonka. "I decided to invite five children to the factory, and the one I liked best at the end of the day would be the winner!"

"But Mr. Wonka," stammered Grandpa Joe, "do you

really and truly mean that you are giving the whole of this enormous factory to little Charlie? After all. . . ."

"There's no time for arguments!" cried Mr. Wonka. "We must go at once and fetch the rest of the family—Charlie's father and his mother and anyone else that's around! They can all live in the factory from now on! They can all help to run it until Charlie is old enough to do it by himself! Where do you live, Charlie?"

Charlie peered down through the glass elevator at the snow-covered houses that lay below. "It's over there," he said, pointing. "It's that little cottage right on the edge of the town, the tiny little one. . . ."

"I see it!" cried Mr. Wonka, and he pressed some more buttons and the elevator shot down toward Charlie's house.

"I'm afraid my mother won't come with us," Charlie said sadly.

"Why ever not?"

"Because she won't leave Grandma Josephine and Grandma Georgina and Grandpa George."

"But they must come too."

"They can't," Charlie said. "They're very old and they haven't been out of bed for twenty years."

"Then we'll take the bed along as well, with them in it," said Mr. Wonka. "There's plenty of room in this elevator for a bed."

"You couldn't get the bed out of the house," said Grandpa Joe. "It won't go through the door."

"You mustn't despair!" cried Mr. Wonka. "Nothing is impossible! You watch!"

The elevator was now hovering over the roof of the Bucket's little house.

"What are you going to do?" cried Charlie.

"I'm going right on in to fetch them," said Mr. Wonka.

"How?" asked Grandpa Joe.

"Through the roof," said Mr. Wonka, pressing another button.

"No!" shouted Charlie.

"Stop!" shouted Grandpa Joe.

CRASH went the elevator, right down through the roof of the house into the old people's bedroom. Showers of dust and broken tiles and bits of wood and cockroaches and spiders and bricks and cement went raining down on the three old ones who were lying in bed, and each of them thought that the end of the world was come. Grandma Georgina fainted, Grandma Josephine dropped her false teeth, Grandpa George put his head under the blanket, and Mr. and Mrs. Bucket came rushing in from the next room.

"Save us!" cried Grandma Josephine.

"Calm yourself, my darling wife," said Grandpa Joe, stepping out of the elevator. "It's only us."

"Mother!" cried Charlie, rushing into Mrs. Bucket's arms. "Mother! Mother! Listen to what's happened! We're all going back to live in Mr. Wonka's factory and we're going to help him to run it and he's given it *all* to me and . . . and . . . and . . . and. . . ."

"What *are* you talking about?" said Mrs. Bucket.

"Just look at our house!" cried poor Mr. Bucket. "It's in ruins!"

"My dear sir," said Mr. Wonka, jumping forward and shaking Mr. Bucket warmly by the hand, "I'm so very glad to meet you. You mustn't worry about your house. From now on, you're never going to need it again, anyway."

"Who *is* this crazy man?" screamed Grandma Josephine. "He could have killed us all."

"This," said Grandpa Joe, "is Mr. Willy Wonka himself."

It took quite a time for Grandpa Joe and Charlie to

explain to everyone exactly what had been happening to them all day. And even then they all refused to ride back to the factory in the elevator.

"I'd rather die in my bed!" shouted Grandma Josephine.

"So would I!" cried Grandma Georgina.

"I refuse to go!" announced Grandpa George.

So Mr. Wonka and Grandpa Joe and Charlie, taking no notice of their screams, simply pushed the bed into the elevator. They pushed Mr. and Mrs. Bucket in after it. Then they got in themselves. Mr. Wonka pressed a button. The doors closed. Grandma Georgina screamed. And the elevator rose up off the floor and shot through the hole in the roof, out into the open sky.

Charlie climbed onto the bed and tried to calm the three old people who were still petrified with fear. "Please don't be frightened," he said. "It's quite safe. And we're going to the most wonderful place in the world!"

"Charlie's right," said Grandpa Joe.

"Will there be anything to eat when we get there?" asked Grandma Josephine. "I'm starving! The whole family is starving!"

"Anything to *eat*?" cried Charlie, laughing. "Oh, you just wait and see!"

AN INTERVIEW WITH
Roald Dahl

This interview, conducted by family friend Todd McCormack, took place in 1988, when Roald Dahl was 71. As Dahl himself said, "I have worked all my life in a small hut up in our orchard. It is a quiet private place and no one has been permitted to pry in there." He not only let Todd McCormack inside the hut, but also gave him rare insight into how he worked, where his ideas came from, and how he shaped them into unforgettable stories. Roald Dahl passed away in 1990, two years after the interview.

WHAT IS IT LIKE WRITING A BOOK?

When you're writing, it's rather like going on a very long walk, across valleys and mountains and things, and you get the first view of what you see and you write it down. Then you walk a bit further, maybe up onto the top of a hill, and you see something else. Then you write that and you go on like that, day after day, getting different views of the same landscape really. The highest mountain on the walk is obviously the end of the book, because it's got to be the best view of all, when everything comes together and you can look back and see that everything you've done all ties up. But it's a very, very long, slow process.

HOW DO YOU GET THE IDEAS FOR YOUR STORIES?

It starts always with a tiny little seed of an idea, a little germ, and that even doesn't come very easily. You can be mooching around for a year or so before you get a good one. When I do get a good one, mind you, I quickly write it down so that I won't forget it, because it disappears otherwise rather like a dream. But when I get it, I don't dash up here and start to write it. I'm very careful. I walk around it and look at it and sniff it and then see if I think it will go. Because once you start, you're embarked on a year's work and so it's a big decision.

HOW DID YOU GET THE IDEA FOR JAMES AND THE GIANT PEACH?

I had a kind of fascination with the thought that an apple—there're a lot of apple trees around here, and fruit trees, and you can watch them through the summer getting bigger and bigger from a tiny little apple to bigger and bigger ones, and it seemed to me an obvious thought—what would happen if it didn't stop growing? Why should it stop growing at a certain size? And this appealed to me and I thought this was quite a nice little idea and [then I had to think] of which fruit I should take for my story. I thought apple, pear, plum, peach. Peach is rather nice, a lovely fruit. It's pretty and it's big and it's squishy and you can go into it and it's got a big seed in the middle that you can play with. And so the story started.

What is your work routine?

My work routine is very simple and it's always been so for the last 45 years. The great thing, of course, is never to work too long at a stretch, because after about two hours you are not at your highest peak of concentration, so you have to stop. Some writers choose certain times to write, others [choose] other times, and it suits me to start rather late. I start at 10 o'clock and I stop at 12. Always. However well I'm going, I will stay there until 12, even if I'm a bit stuck. You have to keep your bottom on the chair and stick it out. Otherwise, if you start getting in the habit of walking away, you'll never get it done.

How do you keep the momentum going when you are writing a novel?

One of the vital things for a writer who's writing a book, which is a lengthy project and is going to take about a year, is how to keep the momentum going. It is the same with a young person writing an essay. They have got to write four or five or six pages. But when you are writing it for a year, you go away and you have to come back. I never come back to a blank page; I always finish about halfway through. To be confronted with a blank page is not very nice. But Hemingway, a great American writer, taught me the finest trick when you are doing a long book, which is, he simply said in his own words, "When you are going good, stop writing." And that means that if everything's going well and you know exactly where the end of the chapter's going to go and you know just what the people are going to do, you don't go on writing and writing until you come to the end of it, because when you do, then you say, well, where am I going to go next? And you get up and you walk away and you don't want to come back because you don't know where you want to go. But if you stop when you are going good, as Hemingway said…then you know what you are going to say next. You make yourself stop, put your pencil down and everything, and you walk away. And you can't wait to get back because you know what you want to say next and that's lovely and you have to try and do that. Every time, every day all the way through the year. If you stop when you are stuck, then you are in trouble!

WHAT IS THE SECRET TO KEEPING
YOUR READERS ENTERTAINED?

My lucky thing is I laugh at exactly the same jokes that children laugh at and that's one reason I'm able to do it. I don't sit out here roaring with laughter, but you have wonderful inside jokes all the time and it's got to be exciting, it's got to be fast, it's got to have a good plot, but it's got to be funny. It's got to be funny. And each book I do is a different level of that. Oh, *The Witches* is quite different from *The BFG* or *James [and the Giant Peach]* or *Danny [the Champion of the World]*. The line between roaring with laughter and crying because it's a disaster is a very, very fine one. You see a chap slip on a banana skin in the street and you roar with laughter when he falls slap on his backside. If in doing so you suddenly see he's broken a leg, you very quickly stop laughing and it's not a joke anymore. I don't know, there's a fine line and you just have to try to find it.

HOW DO YOU CREATE INTERESTING CHARACTERS?

When you're writing a book, with people in it as opposed to animals, it is no good having people who are ordinary, because they are not going to interest your readers at all. Every writer in the world has to use the characters that have something interesting about them, and this is even more true in children's books. I find that the only way to make my characters *really* interesting to children is to exaggerate all their good or bad qualities, and so if a person is nasty or bad or cruel, you make them very nasty, very bad, very cruel. If they are ugly, you make them extremely ugly. That, I think, is fun and makes an impact.

HOW DO YOU INCLUDE HORRIFIC EVENTS WITHOUT SCARING YOUR READERS?

You never describe any horrors happening, you just say that they do happen. Children who got crunched up in Willy Wonka's chocolate machine were carried away and that was the end of it. When the parents screamed, "Where has he gone?" and Wonka said, "Well, he's gone to be made into fudge," that's where you laugh, because you don't see it happening, you don't hear the child screaming or anything like that ever, ever, ever.

HOW MUCH HAS LIVING IN THE COUNTRYSIDE INFLUENCED YOU?

I wouldn't live anywhere else except in the country, here. And, of course, if you live in the country, your work is bound to be influenced by it in a lot of ways, not pure fantasy like Charlie with chocolate factories, witches, and BFG's, but the others that are influenced by everything around you. I suppose the one [book] that is most dependent purely on this countryside around here is *Danny the Champion of the World,* and I rather love that book. And when I was planning it, wondering where I was going to let Danny and his father live, all I had to do, I didn't realize it, all I had to do was look around my own garden and there it was.

ROALD DAHL ON THE SUBJECT OF CHOCOLATE:

In . . . seven years of this glorious and golden decade [the 1930s], all the great classic chocolates were invented: the Crunchie, the Whole Nut bar, the Mars bar, the Black Magic assortment, Tiffin, Caramello, Aero, Malteser, the Quality Street assortment, Kit Kat, Rolo, and Smarties. In music the equivalent would be the golden age when compositions by Bach and Mozart and Beethoven were given to us. In painting it was the equivalent of the Renaissance in Italian art and the advent of the Impressionists toward the end of the nineteenth century. In literature it was Tolstoy and Balzac and Dickens. I tell you, there has been nothing like it in the history of chocolate and there never will be.

Roald Dahl, born in 1916 in

Wales, spent his childhood in England and later worked in Africa. When World War II broke out, he joined the Royal Air Force and became a fighter pilot. After a war injury, he moved to Washington, D.C., and there he began to write. His first short story was published by *The Saturday Evening Post,* and so began a long and distinguished career.

Roald Dahl became, quite simply, one of the best-loved children's book authors of all time. Although he passed away in 1990, his popularity and that of his many books—*Charlie and the Great Glass Elevator, James and the Giant Peach, Danny the Champion of the World,* to name just a few—continues to grow.

Visit www.roalddahl.com to learn more about the author and his books.

※ ※ ※

Quentin Blake has

illustrated most of Roald Dahl's children's books as well as many others. The Children's Laureate of the United Kingdom and a recipient of the Kate Greenaway Medal, Quentin Blake lives in London and teaches illustration at the Royal College of Art.